FICTION
FROM PRISON

DIETRICH BONHOEFFER

FICTION FROM PRISON

Gathering Up the Past

Edited by Renate and Eberhard Bethge

with Clifford Green (in the English Edition)

Translated by Ursula Hoffmann

FORTRESS PRESS   PHILADELPHIA

This book is a translation of *Fragmente aus Tegel. Drama und Roman*, © 1978 Chr. Kaiser Verlag, Munich.

COPYRIGHT © 1981 BY FORTRESS PRESS

Library of Congress Cataloging in Publication Data

Bonhoeffer, Dietrich, 1906–1945
　Fiction from prison

　Translation of: Fragmente aus Tegel.
　Bibliography: p. 171
　Includes index.
　I. Bethge, Renate, 1925-　. II. Bethge, Eberhard,
1909-　. III. Green, Clifford. IV. Title.
PT2603.062F713 1981　　838'.91209　　80–2378
ISBN 0-8006-0663-9　　　　　　　　AACR2

8556K80　Printed in the United States of America　1–663

Contents

Introduction to the English Edition

This book is Dietrich Bonhoeffer's own "introduction" to his celebrated *Letters and Papers from Prison*. Only recently published in Germany, though written in 1943, it sheds fascinating light on his autobiography, theology, and ethics. While other writings by Bonhoeffer have first appeared in the last decade,[1] this is certainly the only one to be published in many years with equal appeal to the general reader and the specialist.

Those who already know the life and writings of Bonhoeffer, which have had such a powerful impact on Christian theology since World War II, will find here invaluable new insights into his familial, social, and intellectual world. Those who are meeting him for the first time will encounter a Christian theologian meditating in a Nazi prison cell on the experiences and convictions which had made him not only a resister of tyranny and death but also, in our eyes, an exemplar of faith and humanity.

The full story of Bonhoeffer's eventful and moving life may be found in Eberhard Bethge's standard biography;[2] a succinct and lively account now appears in the recently translated short biography, *Costly Grace: An Illustrated Introduction to Dietrich Bonhoeffer*, by Eberhard and Renate Bethge.[3]

What was it that brought this son of an upper-middle-class Berlin family of academic and professional people to a Nazi prison cell, writing fiction in a meditation aimed at "gathering up his past"? Perhaps two words may point to the answer: Christian humanism. Both traditions, humanism and Christianity, were embodied in his family, and, not without considerable personal struggle, Bonhoeffer integrated them in himself. After a short but brilliant career as a theologian at the University of Berlin, Bonhoeffer quickly became a leading figure in the Confessing Church after Hitler's rise to power in 1933. His theological and ethical resistance to Nazism was uncompromising from the beginning; so was the opposition of his family, though more often on humanist than Christian theological grounds.

Shortly after the outbreak of war it became clear to Bonhoeffer that his Christian convictions required direct political expression, and he became an active member of the resistance movement which was working to assassinate Hitler, overthrow his regime, and negotiate peace. His brothers and other relatives had led the way into the resistance movement. By the time of his arrest in April 1943, Bonhoeffer and his whole family were deeply involved. "I feel myself so much a part of you all," he wrote to his parents a few weeks later, "that I know that we live and bear everything in common, acting and thinking for one another, even though we have to be separated."[4]

Against this background Bonhoeffer turned to his literary efforts in Tegel Prison. His letters at the time tell quite explicitly what he aimed to do. To his friend Eberhard Bethge he wrote:

> I started on a bold enterprise that I've had in mind for a long time: I began to write the story of a contemporary middle-class family. The background for this consisted of all our innumerable conversations on the subject, and my own personal experiences; in short, it was to present afresh middle-class life as we know it in our own families, and especially in the light of Christianity. It tells of two families on terms of friendship living in a small town. Their children grow up, and as they gradually enter into the responsibilities of official positions, they try to work together for the good of the community as mayor, teacher, pastor, doctor, engineer. You would recognize many familiar features, and you come into it too.[5]

While writing these manuscripts—first in drama form and then as a novel—Bonhoeffer's reflections focused mostly on his past. He wrote an essay called "The Feeling of Time," explaining that it "originated mainly in the need to bring before me my own past in a situation that could so easily seem 'empty' and 'wasted.'"[6] He commented to his parents on the confidence and security gained from "the consciousness of being borne up by a spiritual tradition that goes back for centuries," and said, "It's not till such times as these that we realize what it means to possess a past and a spiritual inheritance independent of changes in time and circumstances."[7] And he revealed to Bethge his feelings of painful separation, homesickness, and longing for family and friends; yet he was confident in the belief that "gathering up the past" had a divine blessing.[8]

In this light we may see Bonhoeffer's prison writings under two orientations: The first year is oriented chiefly to the past, to his family background and earlier experiences of childhood and youth; the second year is oriented chiefly to the future, to the new theology of "religionless Christianity" and his hopes for a new church which would serve the coming generations in a new society after the war.

In other words, *Fiction from Prison* and *Letters and Papers from Prison* are companion pieces.

In another comment Bonhoeffer emphatically assured Bethge that he should not worry about the novel turning out as a roman à clef; earlier, though, he admitted that "there is a good deal of autobiography mixed up in it."[9] We have to view the disclaimer with a good deal of friendly skepticism, for as the Introduction and Notes by Renate and Eberhard Bethge plainly show, Bonhoeffer's "fictional" characters and events draw very heavily upon experiences and people in his family and his circle of friends and acquaintances. We may agree with the German literary historian Walther Killy, who wished that Bonhoeffer had written direct autobiography rather than an indirect and veiled "novel"[10] —though that in itself tells us something about Bonhoeffer. What we can be sure about, however, is that this is not fiction in the sense of pure imaginative construct, but rather autobiography and social memory expressed by imagination in the *form* of drama and fiction.[11]

This highlights one of the most striking features of the book. What Bonhoeffer has done is to lay out for us an imaginatively recreated vision of his social world and cultural milieu. As a theologian Bonhoeffer was a highly autobiographical thinker.[12] His autobiography, however, was not the experience of an isolated individualist but, like the basic pattern of his thinking, intrinsically *social*. Hence his remembrance of his past focuses not on the isolated self but on the family which had nurtured, challenged, and sustained him, and on the society in and for which its members worked and suffered.

Bonhoeffer's social self-disclosure connects directly to a fundamental issue for contemporary theology. Today there is a great deal of concern about the way the ideas and ethics of theologians and churches are shaped by their roots in interest groups (economic, racial, sexual, national) and about which social constituencies are served—intentionally or unconsciously—by the theological positions that are taken. Very few theologians of the first half of the century have themselves directly laid out before us their social world as they experienced and perceived it. That is what Bonhoeffer provides us in this book. Here we find a complex network of attitudes, values, beliefs, and styles of relationship vividly presented. While its value as literature may be slight, its contribution to our understanding of Bonhoeffer cannot be overestimated.

One result of this social portrait is to enliven the debate, begun some years ago,[13] about Bonhoeffer and social class. In her commentary, Ruth Zerner, while cognizant of Bonhoeffer's steps to transcend his social class background, sees evidence of elitism, undemocratic attitudes toward social decision making, antipathy to mass culture, a "conservative, fixed sense of social roles," and a conviction that the "right people" must be "on top."[14] The Bethges, on the other hand, hold that Bonhoeffer's views about leadership and a new social elite rest on beliefs about the meaning of culture (*Bildung*) rather than merely reflecting the conventional influence of social and economic status;[15] they further stress that all his adult life Bonhoeffer was disturbed by, and tried to bridge, the gap between upper-middle class and proletariat. This is not the place to pursue the debate at length, but one comment is pertinent: While both the commentator and the editors can adduce evidence for their readings, they are to a significant degree dealing with different questions. To oversimplify a little, perhaps, Zerner's question may be stated this way: To what extent and in what ways were Bonhoeffer's attitudes and thought shaped by his class background, granted that his social views diverged from merely conventional attitudes? The Bethges' question might be stated as follows: Granted

x

that there were limitations of class background, are these not minimized by the Bonhoeffers' class-transcending beliefs about truly cultured people? In other words, the editors interpret Bonhoeffer largely in terms of his consciously held beliefs, while the commentator is asking about the (probably unconscious) influence of social infrastructure. The latter is a more sociological question, the former more ideational. Both concerns are relevant to the debate, but it may be clarified by recognizing that they are distinct—not identical—concerns.

The result of Bonhoeffer's social and personal self-disclosure here is to make him and his world simultaneously more accessible and more distant. The more clearly Bonhoeffer appears in his own setting, the more vividly we realize how much he belonged to his own sociocultural milieu and historical period. The translation reflects this. German titles and names are preserved. The often formal and indirect styles of speech are preserved. The temptation to conform Bonhoeffer to a too idiomatic and more informal style of language, more familiar to Anglo-Saxon ears, has been resisted. His language, in spite of our wishes today, of course does not reflect later feminist consciousness-raising; but to change this would have been anachronistic, and not faithful to the original.

Yet to recognize this cultural distinctiveness and to see Bonhoeffer's strong and deep roots in his own historical context is not to diminish the continuing stimulus of his legacy. Nor is it to minimize the extent to which he was a pioneer who in many striking ways transcended the boundaries of his own time and place. Indeed, one of the most remarkable aspects of Bonhoeffer's influence is the way it has leaped over boundaries of language, nation, culture, and confession. Not only in Europe and the West but also in Asia, Africa, and Latin America his faith and humanity continue to be a living inspiration to many who are dedicated to justice, peace, freedom from oppression, and human solidarity. Thus to see Bonhoeffer etched more vividly in his own world enables us to evaluate his legacy independently so that we can appropriate it creatively in our own historical times and cultural places.

Although this is a personal book, revealing many rich autobiographical and social details about its author, the theological and ethical content is also very important, though expressed indirectly. This work falls, of course, between Bonhoeffer's *Ethics* (1940-43) and his *Letters and Papers from Prison* (1943-45). Many connections to ideas in both those works have been pointed out by the editors, and careful study will be rewarding for those examining the development of Bonhoeffer's later thought.

However, using this book to help understand Bonhoeffer's intellectual development and to assess his legacy will require particular care. The Introduction includes the observation, originally from the German publisher, that some views and attitudes expressed by the characters "show a Bonhoeffer whom he himself had long outgrown, both theologically and in his actions."[16] But at the same time the notes of the editors make many connections to his other writings—to his *Ethics* and to writings before that, and also to his new ideas in the theological letters which followed this fiction. Thus the editors are not suggesting that all of the ideas in this book belong to an earlier stage of Bonhoeffer's thinking. Clearly, then, careful discrimination is required to properly situate the ideas of this book in Bonhoeffer's personal and intellectual development.

The prominence given to the psychological concept of regression in the German title of Zerner's commentary[17] calls for an explanatory comment. Most readers will be familiar with the Freudian concept of regression as retreating from realistic and appropriate adult behavior to emotions and attitudes characteristic of an earlier stage of development, for example, childhood or adolescence. The distinctions here are chiefly between present and past, realistic and unrealistic feelings and behavior. For Freud regression is a defense mechanism, and it is almost always neurotic. This is not the sense in which Zerner uses the term. Rather she is following Ernst Kris and the psychoanalytic ego psychologists influenced by him. For Kris the chief distinction is between secondary and primary processes. The former include logical thought which is intentional, analytical; the latter involve a relaxation of such processes in modes such as reverie, day dreaming, and fantasy, in which one relives past emotions intensely and vividly. Regression thus becomes a way of recovering one's past and of releasing feelings in the depths of the psyche. Rather than being regarded as neurotic, such regression, when coupled with a clear and rational perception of the meaning of those feelings, yields personal insight which has implications for present behavior; insight, then, is a fusion of primary and secondary processes. This is the sense in which Zerner uses the term *regression*, which she sees as a spring of creativity for all of Bonhoeffer's prison writings.

The German original of this book is a critical edition; that is, it contains all the deletions, additions, corrections, notes, and drafts found in the manuscripts. While a translation can never be a critical edition in the full sense, these variations have all been preserved but are printed in the notes. Many of them are quite routine, though others are more revealing. In one case, for instance, Bonhoeffer accidentally writes "Christoph" (the character who represents himself) instead of "Martin," a younger boy in the family, thereby showing that Martin is in many ways also himself at a younger age.[18] Speeches drafted once or twice before appearing in final form are unusual with Bonhoeffer and show the importance he attached to them; an effort has been made to show in English the similarities and changes in such drafts.

In some respects this translation differs slightly from the original. A few errors of fact and printing have been caught and corrected in the Introduction and Notes. A few revisions and additions are found in Ruth Zerner's commentary. Speech and dialogue are printed in the normal form, whereas Bonhoeffer included it all in paragraphs, usually long. And there is one especially fascinating addition in the notes. In the novel is found a long story about rivalry and friendship between two schoolboys, ostensibly of his father's generation, which deals with themes central to Bonhoeffer's theology and ethics. When the first German edition was published, the Bethges noted that they were unaware of any real-life model for this story, either in Bonhoeffer himself or in his father's experience. After publication a classmate of Bonhoeffer wrote the editors informing them of an incident at the Gymnasium which was surely an inspiration for the story. In short, and not surprisingly, the story was heavily autobiographical.[19] The Introduction and Notes by the editors give many invaluable clues to the correspondences between characters in the fiction and members of Bonhoeffer's family and his friends and acquaintances; Ruth Zerner's commentary also includes such indications.

While other translations from Bonhoeffer's theological works may appear in the future, it is safe to predict that there are none to compare with this. *Fiction from Prison* is unique in combining personal and social disclosure with theological and ethical ideas. In this respect its closest counterpart is undoubtedly *Letters and Papers from Prison*. Though this book does not address the stimulating theological ideas of the *Letters*, it may be seen as a seedbed in which some of those ideas are germinating. All readers of Bonhoeffer will find this a fascinating and rewarding book.

CLIFFORD GREEN

Introduction

After a long period of hesitation it has now been decided to make available the full texts of Bonhoeffer's drama and novel fragments, which he sketched in Tegel Prison in 1943. These texts are even more complete than the previous publications of Bonhoeffer's manuscripts in the sense that his own deletions and corrections are also presented here.

The story of this hesitation itself reflects a piece of the history of Bonhoeffer's influence and reception and also, of course, the history of those who, as his literary executors for more than three decades, have been influenced by various desires and interests. As a result, we could not present an edition of the complete works in a chronologically neat order.[1]

In the first decade of posthumous publications our interest was completely concentrated on the supposedly purely theological works, and particularly on the elements in their theological and ethical discussion that pointed ahead. Thus three extracts from the drama[2] and two from the novel,[3] which seemed to us to belong especially to the context of Bonhoeffer's theological ethics, were included in volume 3 of the collected works (*Gesammelte Schriften*); this volume was published in 1960 with the subtitle "Theology and Congregation."

We cannot deny that the two fragments from 1943 were, of course, especially dear to us from the beginning, particularly because of their autobiographical background. However, Mr. Bissinger (director of Christian Kaiser Verlag, Munich) rightly resisted including these alien elements in the program of a theological publishing house. Who was interested in the private milieu of an author of a rigorously Christ-centered theology? What did these nostalgic meditations on family history have to do with the theology of *The*

Cost of Discipleship and the *Letters and Papers from Prison?* Above all we asked: Should one do this to Bonhoeffer? Should we let him speak publicly through a medium that was not his usual one and that he had never used or chosen during his normal life before his imprisonment? Our concern was intensified by the fact that while these writings quite obviously gave him great joy and completely absorbed him during the first stage of his imprisonment, they simply were not good enough to make any literary claim; and they were all too obviously determined by strong dependence upon his reading during those weeks of nineteenth-century authors such as Stifter and Gotthelf. So their statements appear to contradict the currents of the time, and to show a Bonhoeffer whom he himself had long outgrown, both theologically and in his actions.

These reasons are still valid today, but their weight has diminished. But because they are to be taken seriously, we decided both to do a critical edition and also to request an analytical commentary from a quite different perspective. This the American historian Dr. Ruth Zerner has written for us with great care, wealth of knowledge, and sensitivity.

II

Many things happened on the way to this solution. Theology, through its interaction with psychology, sociology, and contemporary history, has reached a new stage of critical self-consciousness. The insight that Bonhoeffer's theology can hardly be separated from his biography might be seen as diminishing the theology, and nowadays many believe this to be the case. But the opposite is true. For today Bonhoeffer's theology is no longer the property only of the church; his participation in the political resistance against the spirit and actions of National Socialism belongs not only to the history of that time; the man's personal life belongs no longer only to his family. Interest in the whole life of this exemplary person is worldwide.

Thus, ever since the sixties a growing number of doctoral candidates were no longer content with only the excerpts from these writings provided in volume 3 of the *Gesammelte Schriften*, but consulted and used the entire manuscript; indeed, they urged us

2

to allow them to print it along with their dissertations. Meanwhile, several years ago we decided that a literary historian such as Walther Killy, who had meantime discovered Bonhoeffer's biography for himself, might write a commentary. His answer, a refusal in the end, both discouraged us and spurred us on.

> Above all, the novel fragment impressed me greatly, at first for subjective reasons to be sure. In it emerged the long-forgotten world of a solidly upper-middle-class adolescence in the district of Mark Brandenburg, the "values" connected with it, the hopes that one had and the anxieties by which one was ruled. How beautiful it would have been if Bonhoeffer could have turned everything he says here indirectly, between the lines and draped in the style of a novel, directly into autobiography. It is apparent that this was not possible because of the situation and the stage of his life. But precisely here the first difficulty arises. In an analysis of the text one would have to separate its personal aspects (they are obviously very strong), its relation to the time, and its literary qualities, in order to present them. In addition, one would have to be confident of making the "upper-middle-class situation" in the Third Reich comprehensible; one would have to pursue the personal components with due respect; finally, one would have to be equipped to deal with the question of why, and according to what models, such a great intellect takes refuge in a literary form that is not his adequate medium. All these questions conceal abundant snares over which a younger person might walk — I, however, fear them because I am too conscious of them. I have surely worked on the problem of "trivial literature" (*Trivialliteratur*) long enough (much too long); that is exactly what makes me shrink back from a literary phenomenon whose "triviality" is really anything but trivial. . . .
>
> Somewhat simpler is the case of the drama fragment. Doubtless it has much less literary value because the construction is much too transparent and the philosophical intention much too obvious. It is astonishing how much it anticipates [Borchert's] *The Man Outside*, which is also a play to which I have always ascribed much more historical than poetic value. But for just that reason the drama fragment presents the problem of doing justice to Bonhoeffer the theologian who basically isn't up to his own standard in this overdrawn yet extremely moving lot of pictures. It is as if someone selected the completely wrong form for his statement, though this doesn't necessarily say anything against the content at all. Of course one can explain it all, and the more superficially one tried, the easier it would be. But I had some very bad experiences a few years ago with a big radio program

about Borchert; all my discretion could not save me from being fundamentally misunderstood, which I could bear in that case but not in this one. After saying all this I cannot deny that in your position I would consult once more with the publisher about whether one should indeed publish these documents at this particular time. Not that one should conceal them—but do we really gain a more rounded picture of the author from them? Don't they make him more "bourgeois" and time-bound than he was in reality? Don't they place him in a false light?[4]

Meanwhile, recent secondary literature and discussion about Bonhoeffer has focused on the so-called bourgeois and time-bound character of these two pieces, such that it is scarcely possible at this point to withhold the genuine and complete texts without conceding the field to the slogans. These pieces, unabridged, now belong in a complete edition of Bonhoeffer's works. Moreover, the careful reader will notice, significantly, many layers in these products of the first stage of imprisonment; they help to comprehend and interpret the man's biography, his way of thinking, and his commitment.

In addition, as Ruth Zerner makes clear, the fragments are interesting evidence of new creativity being released in the process of necessary "regression"; the flashbacks in this fateful life thus become steps for new visions of the future that lend deeper relevance to the Christian faith in the face of epochal changes. New evidence appears here of influences on Bonhoeffer that were already evident in the earlier publications; for example, that of Nietzsche[5] and of Ibsen are visible in the debates with the "philosophy of life" (*Lebensphilosophie*) that marked Bonhoeffer's early years. Who would finally want to do without the abundant references to contemporary history and family relationships if they are at all interested in the phenomenon of Bonhoeffer?

In view of the form taken by this enormous network of biographical and intellectual history, Bonhoeffer himself knew quite well how strongly these literary endeavors may have been influenced by his unique situation. On 24 June 1943 he casually remarked in a letter to his parents,

In general, a prisoner is no doubt inclined to make up, through exaggerated emotion, for the soullessness and lack of warmth in his surroundings; and perhaps he may react too strongly to anything emotional that affects him personally.[6]

III

The variety of material from Bonhoeffer's own origins is indeed astonishing. But one should be cautious about making too simple and too direct identifications with people from his family and associates. From her knowledge of Maria von Wedemeyer-Weller and Eberhard Bethge, Ruth Zerner provides interesting pointers; however, these still need to be supplemented.

In every character in the two fragments, quite often very different people are combined. Father and Mother of the drama and novel clearly correspond to Bonhoeffer's own parents. But the grandmother too has features of his mother (plus those of his own grandmother and the grandmother of his fiancée), and the major, father of the girl in the novel whom Christoph loves, utters Bonhoeffer's own father's words.

In Franz, the oldest brother in the novel, one recognizes Bonhoeffer's oldest brother Karl-Friedrich, who returned from World War I at the age of nineteen with socialist and antimilitarist views (junking, for example, the badge which had been awarded him as a wounded soldier when he learned it had also been awarded to an officer for falling under a horse while drunk). Karl-Friedrich was the first to read Feuerbach and Zola and to discuss them with the family. But at the same time, Franz in the novel also bears features of Dietrich's brother Klaus, who reacted passionately and often found himself in opposition to others. Distinct traces of Klaus, who despite his basically artistic temperament tended to be conservative, are also found, however, in Christoph of the Tegel fragments. But Christoph represents, above all, Dietrich Bonhoeffer himself. Conversations like those given by Bonhoeffer here in the fragments took place in the family and also, of course, with friends such as Eberhard Bethge—here embodied in the figure of Ulrich—and earlier friends such as Justus Delbrück and Franz Hildebrandt. The character of Klara in the novel can be recognized, despite some differences, as Bonhoeffer's sister Ursula. Bonhoeffer himself also appears in the younger brothers Martin and Little Brother, as well as in the main character Christoph. The threads are so manifold that it is only possible with difficulty to point out the traces of all the people who are visible in Bonhoeffer's two compositions.

With imprisonment denying him access to his family and friends, Bonhoeffer lovingly portrays his parental home with many details of its atmosphere and its more important—and even unimportant—family rules. It was considered ridiculous to go beyond a certain measure of family pride; to have one's portrait painted in uniform or official robes; to give silly or pretentious names to one's children. One didn't talk about money; the children were not supposed to know whether one had much or little, because other things counted as far more important. The house was not furnished in an "elegant" way but in a manner that corresponded to one's tastes and needs, the furniture being made of "the best material." One didn't use fancy names for the living room and dining room. One didn't wear a German schoolcap, and one dressed neither in a mediocre nor a striking fashion—though certain striking clothes had to be tolerated, as the mother preferred picturesque apparel for the children; the boys wore their hair longer than others but got long pants and ties later than usual. But then, too, one was to beware of considering such standards absolute and was to accept the openly different behavior of others. In such matters, no "general teaching and rules of conduct" were given directly.

These similarities with the customs in Bonhoeffer's family are too extensive to pursue every detail here; moreover, they can generally be guessed. Many related matters can be found in the notes.

IV

Ruth Zerner frequently emphasizes that Bonhoeffer tried in his Tegel fragments "to reconcile upper-class and middle-class values," to make "an alliance of bourgeoisie and aristocracy" in view of his engagement to Maria von Wedemeyer.[7] Certainly the von Bremer and Brake families are counterpoised. But there is nothing in Bonhoeffer's texts saying that the von Bremers are regarded as upper-class in contrast to the Brakes as middle-class. The "story told within the story" by which "Bonhoeffer provides a symbolic reconciliation of social classes," according to Ruth Zerner,[8] in fact gives no sign of different social valuation of Hans Brake and Harald von Bremer. One could rather find the opposite assumption: Hans Brake is the "king" of his school class; Harald von Bremer, having joined the class recently as a peer, eventually shares the leadership with Hans Brake, though the latter keeps a small advantage. From the beginning the two respect each other and are brought into relation to each other, while other students—such as Meyer, of course, but also the sensibly independent Paul—are put into a different category.

Incidentally, the novel's Renate von Bremer appears in the dramatic fragment merely as "Renate" (and without any family). So whether she is aristocratic or bourgeois doesn't matter here.

This didn't matter in Bonhoeffer's family either. Of course, from time to time one could criticize and poke fun at the aristocracy— a favorite remark was "illiterate because of high and noble birth." But at the same time the aristocracy were one's own relatives: Hanna, the sister of the mother (Paula, née von Hase), was married to Count Rüdiger von der Goltz; Karl-Friedrich and Christel were married to the von Dohnanyis; the grandmother had been a Countess von Kalckreuth; and her sister, the much loved Aunt Helene, was Countess Yorck von Wartenburg. So Bonhoeffer's "entry into that aristocratic family circle [of his fiancée]"[9] was quite unproblematic.

Ruth Zerner points to Bonhoeffer's use of the word *aristocratic* as though it referred to the social aristocracy; for instance, she quotes Bonhoeffer's remark about clerical tricks that are "far too unaristocratic for the Word of God."[10] But *aristocratic* was used by the family to denote an upright, liberal, chivalrous attitude, and in no way referred only to that which was aristocratic by name and social status.

The family did not distinguish between aristocratic and middle-class people, but rather between the cultured and uncultured; this, however, largely had to do with considerations of personal tact and little with class distinctions.[11] The other and seldom mentioned distinction was between middle class and proletariat, with the aristocracy being included in middle class in this context. Thus Bonhoeffer comments on his literary endeavors: "I began to write the story of a contemporary middle-class family . . . in short, a rehabilitation of middle-class life. . . . The children of two friendly families grow up. . . ."[12] Nobility or aristocracy is not mentioned, despite the *von* Bremers.

Moreover, both pieces show that what really disquieted Bonhoeffer was only the distance between his own upper-middle class and the proletariat, and this caused him to try to clarify and bridge it here; see, for example, the encounters of Christoph and Heinrich, Little Brother and Erich, and his interest in transitional figures such as Ulrich, Paul, and others, which is also part of this concern. Bonhoeffer's awareness of the other person as limit is clearly evident in these characters and encounters. Above all: Every time Christoph vehemently propounds his philosophy of the responsibility of a small elite, Bonhoeffer (as author) has someone forcefully interrupt him (that is, himself as character); so it is, for example, in the replies of Heinrich, Franz, and also of the major and the old teacher and, very painfully, in Renate's apprehensive rejection. Naturally, Bonhoeffer — like anyone who is thinking of getting married — considered the way his fiancée's family would match up with his own, and the families von Bremer and Brake represent, of course, his fiancée's family and his own. The basic similarity he saw in both families, even in individual personal traits, is striking. In this respect he writes about Renate von Bremer that "she considered any exhibition of inner personal processes reprehensible and exercised the utmost self-control."[13] Similarly he writes about the Brake family that "one didn't talk about such personal matters but came to terms with them on one's own."[14]

One can sense, incidentally, that Bonhoeffer considers reserve "about such personal matters" as something positive. Such characteristics as self-appraisal, self-confrontation, and self-scrutiny, which Ruth Zerner sees so clearly in him, would surely have made him feel somewhat uncomfortable.[15]

Nevertheless, Ruth Zerner is not far off the mark. Bonhoeffer included the values and ideas of his family origins in this self-examination, and the strength of his support for these ideas is clear. He was aware of the broad-mindedness of his parental home, resulting from his mother's nondoctrinaire Christianity and his father's critical yet open-minded way of thinking and judging. The essence of this family spirit he sketched in his *Ethics* when reflecting on the nature of culture (*Bildung*).[16] He would have liked to see more of this spirit in the church, and that was certainly part of his motivation for writing theology. "The limitations of [his] class background"[17] existed, of course, but surely to a minimal extent. Often enough he spoke of the "narrow horizon" of his colleagues in the church. He did not bring a wider Christian perspective from the church to his family, but on the contrary tried to bring the wider perspective of his family into the sphere of his church and theology. He had found "a multi-dimensional life"[18] in his family and lived it himself.

It is true, of course, that through his concept of "unconscious Christianity" Bonhoeffer included "the nonreligious among his family and friends" in the Christian sphere.[19] The theme of "unconscious Christianity" had already engaged him at an earlier time in conversations with his brother-in-law, Rüdiger Schleicher, who had liked to speak of the "anima christiana naturaliter" (Tertullian).

Ruth Zerner is concerned with the question of why Bonhoeffer does not focus on the atrocious evil of his time but instead deals with trivial, everyday evils.[20] She compares Bonhoeffer with the Jewish writer Elie Wiesel, who survived a concentration camp, and thinks Bonhoeffer's deficiency might derive from his not yet knowing "the full sense of national shame and horror," and his not living "to face in the postwar world the irrepressible implications of the aggregate facts of the Nazi Final Solution."[21] Naturally, nobody knew *everything* before 1945, but what was known to the people around Bonhoeffer was already so incredible as to oblige them to join the Resistance. The attempt to do something against the horror demanded silence, work in the underground. To write something about the final solution, and thus to endanger further not only one's own life but also the lives of one's associates, would have been madness. Ruth Zerner is naturally right, though, to emphasize that the atrocity of the concentration camps was incomparably more terrible than Bonhoeffer's situation in prison.

But Bonhoeffer was also convinced that the basis for all really great evil was already to be found in banal evils, and that the two cannot actually be separated. "I detest such behavior. Much evil, much unhappiness will come from it in our country," he has the major in the novel say about the forester's assistant, the representative of "banal" evil.[22] Again he writes: "These tormentors of men that you find everywhere nowadays, in schools, in offices, in the military. One must engage in battle against them, in pitiless, ruthless battle."[23] And a little later: "Many right-minded people of our class have acquired the habit of smiling about these petty tyrants and of regarding as fools those who have declared total war on them. But smiling about them is as foolish and irresponsible as smiling about the tiny size of bacteria."[24]

V

Now a few remarks about the character of the manuscript, its date, and the formalities of this publication.

There are clear indications in Bonhoeffer's letters (especially those of 17 August and 18 November 1943)[25] for dating the two fragments—the drama in the spring and early summer of 1943, the novel in the summer and winter of 1943. The letters also enable us to interpret Bonhoeffer's different attitudes and ideas during the two years in Tegel: on the one hand there is the tormented yet happy review of his past in 1943, during the time of his first prison experiences and the hearings with all their problems; on the other hand there is much greater serenity for the new forward-looking themes in 1944, during the months when he simply waited for decisions that lay beyond his reach and influence.

The manuscript provides a few additional indications about its date. The drama, consisting of forty-six pages, was written first, in ink; most of it is on four-page sheets of a foolscap-like *Konzeptpapier*, while the last six sheets (that is, twelve pages) are on Din A4 square-lined letter-pad paper [Deutsche Industrie Norm A4 is a standard letter-size paper, in dimensions just under 8½ by 11½ inches.]. The novel, consisting of one hundred nineteen pages, begins with this same square-lined letter-pad paper (eleven sheets, twenty-two pages), and then continues to the end on four-page yellowish *Konzeptpapier* of inferior quality. The use of the square-lined letter paper can be dated precisely because the letters to his parents were written on it only during the period 24 June 1943 to 13 September 1943.[26] The wedding sermon in May 1943 was also written on this paper,[27] and so were a few of the notes on the hearings and drafts of letters to Dr. Roeder, Councillor of the Supreme War Tribunal.[28] This means that Bonhoeffer shifted from the drama to the novel almost exactly at the end of the hearings in July 1943. In his letter of 17 August, in which he announces the shift from drama to narrative, he also makes a request: "I would like some *Konzeptpapier*."[29]

The notes on the hearings, written for Dr. Roeder, are in part also sketched in pencil on that very thin, transparent copy paper on which two almost illegible drafts for the drama have been scribbled: one is the piece of paper with the list of characters and the projections for the scenes,[30] which therefore must have been made after the writing had begun; the other is a piece of paper with a first draft of that speech by Christoph about silence, and sacrifice for Germany which could not be prematurely interpreted, a kind of "political arcane discipline"[31] —this speech was certainly especially important to Bonhoeffer, and he wrote it three times —something he very rarely did.

Within the text, which is all written in ink, there are here and there penciled cue-like notes in the margin, which undoubtedly were added in the evening after Bonhoeffer had stopped writing, or in between stretches of writing, to remind himself of what would have to be improved or changed. We have marked all these programmatic notes (here printed in the notes at the end of the book) "marginal note."

Obvious mistakes in writing are usually noted as such, though those in the titles or names are noted only when they first appear. The many words, sentences, or passages deleted by Bonhoeffer himself are all included in the notes, since they might be significant for understanding the process of Bonhoeffer's writing and for interpreting it. Attention is not drawn, however, to changes which only involve transpositions and similar matters.

The notes are of three types. Some show the state of the text, with its alterations, deletions, or idiosyncrasies. Some point to similarities and patterns of ideas in other works of Bonhoeffer. And some, finally, try to explain certain characters, formulations, events, and situations. Important particulars in these matters were given to us by Bonhoeffer's sisters—Susanne Dress, Ursula Schleicher, and Sabine Leibholz.

We have included in the volume two other small documents which, like Dietrich Bonhoeffer's drama and novel fragments, focus upon his parental house, though they are quite different in character from his; they were written much earlier by his brother Klaus and by Emmi, née Delbrück, Klaus's wife. Both pieces were written for birthdays of the mother, Klaus's being amusing and satirical while Emmi's is carefully weighed, combining both distance and closeness.

As previously, Ulrich Kabitz of Christian Kaiser Verlag aided both the form and the commentary of the whole volume by his expertise in the subject matter and his sensitivity.

May 1978   RENATE AND EBERHARD BETHGE

Drama

[Outline, written in pencil]

Father	Little Brother	Old Gypsy Woman
Christoph —	Grandmother	Physician
war veteran,	Fiancée	Minister
student, age 25	Friend	Students
Sister	Mother	

1. Living room, Grandmother and Little Brother (sister?)
   then Mother; then Father;
   finally Christoph—talk about
   students, fiancée, and friend.
   from: "I'll go write something!" "What?"—
   to . . . [illegible],
   that I wouldn't like to speak about it."
2. Christoph's study.
   Books, harpsichord, lute, pictures?
   Friend and fiancée. Little Brother.
   Alone.
3. Students' party, fiancée—early morning at home.
   Grandmother. Already awake? Watching sunrise.
4. On a trip with friend (and Little Brother?). Gypsy. Stranger
   who tells the truth.
   Minister, whether one must always tell the truth?[1]
5. Little Brother's bedroom—Grandmother and Little Brother
   later Christoph.
6. Christoph's study.
   Alone, now only Little Brother
   are you thinking about God?[2]
   Yes, I think how he . . . [illegible]
   Germany

13

SCENE 1

Living room in an upper-middle-class house. Evening. Grand-mother and Little Brother[3] are sitting at a table on which is a lamp. The grandmother is about seventy, dressed simply. Little Brother, about ten, with the type of clothes worn by boys of his age. He listens very attentively while the grandmother reads to him.

GRANDMOTHER (*reading*): ". . . The hunter had stalked the wonder-ful animal for many days and weeks.[4] Several times he had had it in his sights, but didn't shoot. He couldn't stop feasting his eyes on the magnificence of this creature. But one evening at sunset it so happened that the animal stepped out of the woods right in front of him, looked at him with very calm eyes, and stood there without fear. Never before had the hunter seen the animal like that. A wild longing seized him to have it, not to give it up, not to let it escape again. He loved the animal so much that he could not part from it anymore. Very slowly he lifted his gun, eye to eye with the animal, a last long glance, a long lingering; then came the shot.[5] Afterward all was very quiet, and the last rays of the evening sun fell reconcilingly and peacefully on the fallen crea-ture and its hunter." (*She closes the book and puts it down.*) This is where we stop today, Little Brother. The end of the story is not in the book. But it most certainly continues; as a matter of fact, it really begins at this point.

LITTLE BROTHER: Yes, Grandmother. The story can't end like that at all. But why did the animal look at the hunter so calmly and not run away? Didn't it know that he would shoot it? Wasn't it afraid of that?

GRANDMOTHER: Who knows, child? Perhaps it is as people say, that animals know nothing of death—but then why are they so shy by nature? But perhaps this wonderful animal knew its hunter and realized that it couldn't escape him. And perhaps it sensed the hunter's great love and therefore loved him a little too, and therefore looked at him with such calm, fearless eyes. Perhaps it knew that its death was close and yet did not fear it.[6] Who knows, child?

14

LITTLE BROTHER: Yes, Grandmother, only the animals and God can know. But all people know that they have to die, don't they, Grandmother?

GRANDMOTHER: Yes, they all know—(*after some hesitation*) but in a quite different way. (*after a short, reflective pause*) I'll try to explain it to you. You know you have good parents whom you want to make very happy.

LITTLE BROTHER: Yes, Grandmother, I know.

GRANDMOTHER: But though you know it, you keep forgetting and do things which you wouldn't do if you thought of Father or Mother.

LITTLE BROTHER: Yes, Grandmother.

GRANDMOTHER: But sometimes you feel that Father or Mother are very close to you even if you don't see them, and then you do only what they would like, don't you?

LITTLE BROTHER: Yes, Grandmother.

GRANDMOTHER: You see, that's exactly the way it is with people knowing about dying. They know they have to die, but most forget it for the greater part of their lives. Some don't forget it, and one notices that about them. And then there are a very few who sense when death will come to them. They see it coming. They are quite different from other people.

LITTLE BROTHER: Would you like to be one of those who know when death comes to them, Grandmother?

GRANDMOTHER: We can't and mustn't wish for that, child. That is a gift or a punishment from God.

LITTLE BROTHER: I don't understand that.

GRANDMOTHER: No, you don't. But now it's time to sleep. We'll talk more about these things. Go to bed. Your father is late again; he has a lot of patients in town. And when he comes home, he'll be very tired and will want to be alone with your mother for a while. Good night, child. May God watch over you!

LITTLE BROTHER: Good night, Grandmother. May God watch over you! (*Starts to leave; meets his mother coming in the door.*)

MOTHER (*embracing the child*): Sleep well, my dear boy. Did Grandmother tell you a nice story? Sweet dreams, my dear, my— only child.

LITTLE BROTHER: But Mother. I am not your only child. Did you forget Christoph?

MOTHER (*upset*): No, no, my boy. You are not my only child—no, believe me, I did not forget Christoph. Good night now, and hurry up, it's late. I am waiting up for your father and Christoph.

LITTLE BROTHER (*exits—from outside*): Say hello to Christoph when he comes.

GRANDMOTHER: Would you like to be alone, Anna?

MOTHER: No, I don't want to be alone; I would like to talk to you till Hans gets home. (*She walks over to the grandmother and sits down by her.*) Mother, it can't go on like this. I don't understand it any more. It's the first time in the twenty-five years of our marriage that I no longer understand Hans.[7] It's the first time that he doesn't answer my questions, that he is evasive. And yet, he is more loving and considerate than ever before. But I can see how unhappy he is, how he lies awake for hours at night beside me, how he goes to work tired in the morning and often stays out until late at night. It's been going on for a month now, since . . . Christoph came home. Haven't you noticed how he avoids the boy, how he often looks at him deeply disturbed without saying a word, how he no longer plays with the child, how he no longer touches the piano? Don't you feel that he often talks as if he were far, far away, without seeing us?

GRANDMOTHER: I did notice, child, from the first day that Christoph came to him—to us. Since then he has been living in a different world.[8]

MOTHER: Mother, I don't understand any of that and don't want to, either. Christoph comes back from the war. He was a boy when he left, now he is a man. But he stayed the same; I tell you, he stayed the same. He has not turned into a stranger. Tonight he is with Renate; he stayed faithful to her through all these years. No, Christoph stayed the same, I know it. He is as close to us as he always was.

GRANDMOTHER: Yes, very close, closer than ever and yet very distant, very distant, just as distant as Hans often is now.

MOTHER: Mother, don't say such things which one can't understand. Don't you sense how close he is to you, how he likes to be with you till very late at night, how he loves Little Brother, plays with him and has long talks with him, how early in the morning he seeks out the garden, the flowers, and the sun and enjoys them?

GRANDMOTHER: Yes, grandmothers, children, and gardens . . . they are usually distant to a young man. For him they are curiously close. I can hear Hans coming and I'll leave you two alone. (*aside*) May God grant that he finds the courage to speak out. (*Exits.*)

MOTHER (*speaking to herself*): Good God, it can't be true.

FATHER (*Enters, a man of fifty-five, dressed like a doctor; he looks tired. Wordlessly walks over to his wife, kisses her and says with warmth and some compassion*): Anna, my dear.

MOTHER: It's very late again, Hans.

FATHER: I had a lot to do in town.

MOTHER (*somewhat expressionlessly*): Yes, I suppose there is always a lot to do nowadays.

FATHER: The aftermath of war.

MOTHER (*more emphatically, aside*): Yes, the aftermath of the war. Are you hungry? Or shall I bring you something to drink? Ulrich's parents sent a few bottles of red wine today as thanks for the aid to Ulrich and to celebrate Christoph's homecoming and recovery. It was very kind of them. They are very fond of Christoph.

FATHER (*who was about to agree heartily, completely changed his expression at the mention of Christoph's name*): No, thank you, Anna, I don't want anything to drink now. Christoph shall have these bottles for a celebration with his friends. No, really, thank you. I'll drink nothing now. Did Mother retire?

MOTHER: Yes, she went when she heard you come and wanted to leave us alone. She thought we might have something to talk about with each other. But—she might just as well have stayed.

FATHER: Of course she could have stayed. I, at least, have nothing, really nothing at all which . . . By the way, did Ulrich come to see you? He wanted to see you right after his release from the military hospital. He is just fine. He is more lively and sparkling

17

than ever. (*pause*) It's a miracle that everything worked out so well; it had looked bad; I didn't have much hope. Yes, miracles do happen sometimes.

MOTHER: Ulrich was here briefly, he asked about Christoph and Renate. Then he went to see them. He is extremely fond of Christoph, and I am so happy for Christoph that he has him, especially now.

FATHER: Yes, it seems that times are coming when one needs true friends.'

MOTHER: That's not what I meant.

FATHER: Let it go, Anna; I saw things today—I'd give a lot never to have seen them. A wounded young soldier, about Christoph's age, was hobbling across the street on crutches. Behind him walked two very healthy, foppish young men of about the same age. I saw one of them point his finger at the wounded man, smile disgustingly, and say in a voice loud enough for all to hear, "That's another one of those ever-stupid ones; there are still too many of them!" (*pause*) I thought then, Anna, it's better to be dead than to hear that.

MOTHER: And what did you do, Hans?

FATHER: What could I do? I didn't have the one thing I needed— I have no weapon. (*increasingly excited*) Anna, there is nothing that would be baser and more unnatural, there is no more damnable crime, more deserving of death, than this mockery of a victim. Yes, Anna, I would have fired truly, even though I knew I would be doing something wrong. What did I do? Nothing at all—I ran after the louts, I grabbed their collars, shook them so that they swayed about, I couldn't get a word out. I was shaking with rage myself. The wounded man stopped, turned around—I knew him, he was a patient from my hospital. He smiled gratefully and seemed a little embarrassed or ashamed. Meanwhile the rabble had crowded around us and started coming at me. A policeman came, wanted to take down my name; when he heard it and when a voice from the crowd I couldn't recognize said, "That is the medical superintendent from the military hospital"—he looked at me for a moment in astonishment, slowly nodded his head a few times as if he had understood something,

18

and let me go. The two louts flagged down a taxi and got in smiling. The wounded man said goodbye and left; I stood there and said to myself, "Better dead than this!" At that moment Christoph suddenly appeared next to me and said, "Yes, Father, you are right, better dead than this!"

MOTHER: Hans!

FATHER: What is the matter, Anna? Does that frighten you? There'll be more things like that and much worse. God, what a world we have brought our children into! Sometimes I think it would be better — if they had never been born.

MOTHER: Hans, what are you talking about?

FATHER (*severely*): Anna, be quiet. You don't understand that — you can't. You don't see the world as it is.[10] What kind of life is it to see every day, from morning to night, young people with shot-up limbs and torn bodies, destroyed hopes, ruined happiness; and if miraculously we manage to save one, beside him is another who can only expect death. What business has a young person with death, Anna? If he were meeting it at the front, if death got him suddenly in the midst of action, in battle — then it would be merciful. But a slow, creeping, yet certain death — and without hope of seeing a different, better time. (*with the utmost excitement*)[11] What kind of life is that? (*Paces the room, then stops; becomes very calm.*) — Excuse me, please, excuse me — where else can I say all this except with you? (*Kisses her.*)

MOTHER: You have not said everything yet, Hans.

FATHER (*after a pause*): No, I have not said everything yet, Anna. (*pause, then reporting very calmly*) About a month ago when Christoph came home, barely healed, his appearance worried me. One morning I made him come to see me in the hospital and examined him. I couldn't help it — since then I have known. . . .

MOTHER: Yes, since then you have known.[12]

FATHER: Yes, Anna — poor, poor Anna.

MOTHER (*as if from afar*): So it's true. How much longer does Christoph have?

FATHER: A year at most.

MOTHER: You said nothing to Christoph?

FATHER: Nothing.

MOTHER: He suspects nothing?

FATHER: He can't, since he has no pain, and presumably won't until the end.

MOTHER: Thank God—no one else knows? No doctor, no nurse, no friend?[13]

FATHER: No one aside from you and me.

MOTHER: Then no one will learn it from us. (*long pause*) Hans, I'll tell you how it will be. We will live with Christoph for an incredibly happy year. For his sake we will not permit ourselves to feel sorrow for him. We will only be happy for him and with him. We will grant his wish for a trip to the mountains. We will not have to hide any tears from him because there will be nothing but gladness in our hearts—to the last day. The sun shall set brilliantly over his life. Hans, let us promise each other. There must be no pain, no sadness, no bitterness in us now. Christoph would sense it, and we would be doing a great wrong to him and to ourselves. Hans, let us bear together not the pain but our happiness about our son.

FATHER: Anna, what a wife, what a mother you are!

(*There is a knock on the door.*)

CHRISTOPH (*enters*): Good evening, Mother, good evening, Father. How nice to see you still up. Where is Grandmother? How is Little Brother?

MOTHER: Grandmother told Little Brother the story of the hunter and the wonderful animal; then they went to bed. Little Brother says hello. You are coming back from Renate? Did Ulrich find you two?

CHRISTOPH: Yes, I was with Renate, and later Ulrich and I went to our group. Everybody is talking about what happened this morning. How are you, Father? If only I had arrived a moment earlier, I would have taken over for you. It was awful to see you in that rabble. By the way, the policeman was the father of someone in our group.

FATHER: What do they think about the incident?

CHRISTOPH: You know, Father, that we agree on such matters, and no one would easily say anything against you; nearly all of them know you, after all. Only one was there, a newcomer, who didn't say a word; I don't know where he comes from. He is terribly patched up, awfully pale and sick, and looks frightfully bitter. Some kind of hatred is in him. He looks very intelligent and not a bad fellow. But he seemed to have a different opinion from ours. I don't know what it was or why. When I said goodbye to him, he looked at me strangely as if he wanted something, but he didn't say anything.

FATHER: A few months ago I had a chap like that in the hospital; they brought him in in a nearly hopeless condition; he was terribly wounded, a man with a good, intelligent head. We fought for his life day and night. He didn't say a word; he usually lay in bed with his eyes closed, but his mouth was bitter. When I was at his bedside, he would briefly open his eyes sometimes and look at me in a way I couldn't interpret; there was something in it of deadly hatred and something like the fervent plea of a child. We managed no more for him than some patchwork which may last for a few years, perhaps. Even when he was better he kept up his reserve. Finally he had to be released; we had done everything possible for him. I won't forget how this young man, whose life we had saved for at least a few years, came to my room to say goodbye, looked at me with flickering eyes, and told me in passionate excitement: "Why didn't you let me die? By your skill you managed to bully a few years out of God for my life; these years will be the devil's. Whatever happens now will be your fault alone. I can't bear this life without becoming very bad." I stood as if destroyed; I don't remember what I did. I think I told him I wanted to help, that he should come back. I have not seen him again. Perhaps it is the same man you were talking about, Christoph?

CHRISTOPH: I'll speak to him, Father. Aside from that, it was a heated evening again. In connection with the incident, someone started to talk about the right of free speech, and finally we were right back in the debate about the freedom of the citizen. It was a heated argument. Father, I maintained that one should never make freedom a slogan for the masses, because from that would arise the worst kind of slavery. I said that freedom is only for the very few, noble, select people.[14] For the others, however, law and order must take its place. I also said that there must be upper and lower positions among men, and whoever doesn't grasp that brings chaos to the people. And finally, I even said that there are men, noble by nature, who are destined to rule and be free, and that there are people who are by nature rabble, and they must serve. Nothing is more frightful and destructive than to undo this order so that the rabble rules and the noble serve. But these two kinds of people differ in that the rabble knows only how to live, while the noble know also how to die. Do you agree, Father? Yes, surely you do, or else you wouldn't have said today, "Better dead than this!" They almost throttled me for what I said, and next time I am supposed to justify my arguments.[15]

MOTHER: Christoph,[16] I suppose none of you really understands these things yet. What does Ulrich think?

CHRISTOPH: Ulrich is always on my side; I can depend on him.

MOTHER: I don't want to get in the way of your plans, son. But I wanted to suggest something to you today anyway. After all, you are not quite recovered yet, but you want to be well soon. How about you and Ulrich and, if you want, also Little Brother taking a nice trip to the mountains?

CHRISTOPH: Mother—to the mountains! Yes, I'd like that. Thank you both. Is it true that Ulrich's parents sent some wine today? Then let's drink a glass of wine to this plan.

FATHER (*gets up, fetches a bottle, opens it, not looking at Christoph while he pours*): It was sent to celebrate your recovery, Christoph, so let's drink to that. To your health, my son!

CHRISTOPH: To you, Father, Mother!

(*They clink glasses. Christoph's glass breaks. Silence for a moment.*)

LITTLE BROTHER (*in his nightclothes*): I can't sleep; I keep seeing the hunter and the wonderful animal who love each other so much—Christoph, you are home!

CHRISTOPH (*takes Little Brother on his knee*): Come here, Little Brother, relax, I'll tell you something nice: Soon I am going to the high mountains with Ulrich, and perhaps, perhaps if you are good and our parents permit it—you can come with me everywhere. Only if I climb a very high mountain top, you stay below, but then wave at me and I will see you below until I am at the very top, all right? Now go back to bed and dream about it, and tomorrow ask Father and Mother in a nice way if you may come. (*Little Brother exits.*)

MOTHER (*has meanwhile unobtrusively brought a new glass*): Once again, to a good trip, Christoph (*they clink glasses*), and good night. Don't stay up too long. We are tired, it was a long day. Good night.

(*Father and Mother exit quickly.*)

CHRISTOPH (*alone, takes the pieces of the glass and drops them slowly*): Thank God — they suspect nothing! (*Takes a photograph from his pocket, looks at it for a long time.*) — Renate!

(*Curtain*)

SCENE 2

Christoph's study in the style of a student's room, with books, pictures. A desk with a lot of handwritten papers. He is sitting at the harpsichord, playing "Farewell to the Klavier" by C.P.E. Bach.[17] *Afternoon.*

Ulrich enters unnoticed while Christoph is playing; quickly steps behind him; suddenly puts his hands over Christoph's eyes.

CHRISTOPH: Renate!

ULRICH (*laughs aloud.*)

CHRISTOPH: Oh, it's you, Ulrich. Stop that nonsense; always tricks. (*Turns around toward him and looks at him smiling.*) But it's good to see you anyway.

ULRICH: Melancholy again?[18] (*reaches for the music and reads*) "'Farewell to the Klavier' by C.P.E. Bach." What's got into you? You have hardly come back to your harpsichord, which you missed so terribly, and now you want to take leave of it again? Say, have you lost your mind? Come, sit here and say something sensible.

(*They sit down in easy chairs, fill their pipes from a tobacco jar, and light up.*)

CHRISTOPH: If you really want to hear something sensible, I'll tell you: I do indeed lose my mind from time to time.

ULRICH: So! Too bad! Unfortunately I haven't noticed that yet. Yesterday evening, for instance, your head was very much together, as you ought to know yourself.

CHRISTOPH: You haven't noticed yet, since I only lose it when I am alone, and even then—with luck—only occasionally. What would you think of a promising young man of twenty-four who for a month has been catching himself, again and again, talking aloud to himself?

ULRICH: Well, anyway—quite a good start! It's really a pity about the promising young man of twenty-four!

CHRISTOPH: You can't imagine losing your mind some day, can you, Ulrich?

ULRICH: Well, I don't have as much mind to lose as you—but let me think for a moment—perhaps if I were terribly in love? But no, I think even then I have kept my senses quite nicely up to now—or—I have got it (*gets up, acts it out*): If a man in black with a deadly serious expression came to see me today, to tell me solemnly, "Sir, permit me to make the regrettable announcement that unfortunately tomorrow you are going to be executed." If he said "the day after tomorrow," it would be different; then I probably wouldn't lose my mind until tomorrow.[19] To be serious, Christoph, that just reminded me of a conversation I had with the newcomer on the way home last night; it wasn't funny at all. That's really why I came today. You saw him too, the one with the black hair who was sitting there all evening without opening his mouth. I felt like making him talk. After all, he could have been a spy, and as you said yesterday, those are the types we have the least use for. So I walked him home. I asked him whether he had liked our group. He answered nothing at all at first, and then suddenly, a bit scornfully, "Who is that young aristocrat who was airing his wild theories today?" I said, "There are no aristocrats among us, but if you mean the tall blond man who was the only one to say something sensible today—that is my friend, son of the medical superintendent at the military hospital." At that he mumbled to himself, but in a way that I was meant to hear, "Oh, that too, the son of the doctor who deprived me of my life, or rather, my well-deserved death." I was completely taken aback. After a long time he then asked, "He isn't going to last very long, either, is he?" and pointed at his heart.

CHRISTOPH: So, is that what he said?

ULRICH: Yes, I thought he must be crazy and asked, "What are you talking about?" Whereupon he said, "I thought you were his friend, and you haven't noticed a thing yet, have you?" You know, I usually have no trouble finding something to say. But he said all of that with such a cold decisiveness, and in such a tone of voice as if he knew something mysterious, that I felt as though someone were pouring ice water down my back. For some time I walked beside him in silence and felt like bidding him farewell as soon as possible. Then suddenly he started up again: "I like you, you are honest; but your friend, he is pretending to himself and to you all. Watch him." I wanted to say, "What is the matter with you, you know neither me nor my friend, and you are playing the grand psychologist." But for some reason I was silent again, and angry with him and my own stupidity. Then he asked again, quite out of the blue, "Can you take a blow?" "Talk," I replied. I shuddered again and again, but I couldn't back out. What followed after that I can't recount to you in detail; it was a life story, a confession if you will—but he didn't swear me to silence. He even said, at the end, "Tell your friend if you want to, and say hello to him."

CHRISTOPH: So, go on.

ULRICH: Here are the highlights, at least: He didn't know his parents. His father was in prison for many years because of some bad affair—he didn't say what—and died there. He grew up near the harbor, in his aunt's tavern, among sailors and prostitutes. When he was old enough to begin understanding what was going on around him—I'll have to say this in his own words: "Suddenly I met God in the midst of hell."[20] By chance he got hold of a picture, probably similar to Rembrandt's "Hundred Guilder Print," with Christ healing the poor, and underneath two biblical quotations, "He had compassion on the multitude" and "The tax collectors and harlots will inherit the Kingdom of God before you," or something like that.[21] Then began, he said, a terrible battle for him. He stayed in the same environment and gradually grew up. He tried, as he put it, to live in hell with God. Running away seemed cowardly to him. He became a dockworker. At night he read books about—political economy, social legislation, and especially the Bible. When he came home from work, he got loafing children off the street, took them to his room, gave them food, said something kind to them, and sent them home. But the stifling atmosphere and misery around him got to be too much for him.[22] He met a prostitute who loved him very much. He gave her money—but never went to her, "from sorrow and from respect for Christ," as he said in his strange way of speaking.[23] But he was never pious, he said; he didn't go to church. "I never felt the urge, either, to work as a social reformer or a preacher; all of that is no good. But I could no longer forget God, and wanted to live in my hell with him, from sorrow." All of the ideas and occasional proposals of his bosses to get ahead, go to high school, university, and so on, he rejected. It would only have been an escape, he said, and he might have forgotten God and his sorrow. "I always knew that I wouldn't have long to live, and it made me glad." This was about how he expressed it.

CHRISTOPH: So, that's what he said.

ULRICH: Yes, and then the war came. It was a release for him. He had the feeling he had made it now. He counted on being killed. "I know that is what God wanted," he said. It seems he distinguished himself by extraordinary valor and concern for his comrades. He got the Iron Cross, Second Class, after carrying three wounded comrades, one after the other, from under fire in the front lines back into the trenches. He told me that only after I had asked. Soon afterward he was also awarded the Iron Cross, First Class. But he refused to be promoted. He has a letter from his captain who promised personally to take care of his education after the war. Then he was seriously wounded. Before fainting he told a comrade, "Take care no one wakes me; I am so happy; I have found *my* death; I am through." After many weeks, he woke up in your father's hospital. They had done everything humanly possible to save his life. "This awakening was my end," he said. "Since then, I have been hating God and man. It was clear to me immediately, and every breath confirmed it, that my life had only been artificially lengthened by one or two years. What good is this life to me? I can't return to my hell where I had God; I have no strength left. Studying and whatever else they propose and want to help with—oh, these compassionate people!—that doesn't belong in *my* life, and moreover I could no longer do it. I used up my strength before and during the war. Nothing is left, and because this is no life, I also can no longer bear the thought of death. Oh, these clever, compassionate people, how they have cheated God and me. God wanted my death; it came at the right time. The people wanted my life, and now I am the devil's. Good night! Tell your friend if you want to, and say hello to him." With that, he turned right at a corner and disappeared.

CHRISTOPH: Strange, very strange.

ULRICH: Believe me, I lay awake for a long time—not until the sun shone into my room so brilliantly this morning did I shake off last night's conversation like a nightmare. I really shudder to see him again.

CHRISTOPH: I'll visit him. He isn't crazy or bad, and he's definitely not stupid. He is merely very lonely. But he seems to know something.

ULRICH: I beg you, Christoph, don't go to see him, he'll only put crazy ideas into your head. You can do without those, and besides, he is very suspicious of you. Go see Renate; that is better for you, and moreover you owe her a visit and an explanation for your strange behavior yesterday afternoon.

CHRISTOPH: Renate!

ULRICH: What's the matter with you, Christoph? Nowadays you are sometimes unpredictable. You needn't go to her house, by the way; I just met her in the street. She was wearing the light dress which you like so much on her, and she looked, again, so infinitely good and kind; you don't deserve that at all. She asked how you were; how it had been last night; when we went home; when you are usually to be found in your room. She appeared to be a bit worried, and I think she'll come by here.

CHRISTOPH: Ulrich, that mustn't happen.

ULRICH: But Christoph, why is that? It's getting so I can't understand you at all any more. Did Renate hurt you in some way—or . . .

CHRISTOPH (*severely*): I tell you, Ulrich, it must not happen. (*after a pause*) You know too that the whole thing has been a friendship since we were children and that I never said or did anything to tie her to me.[24]

ULRICH (*completely surprised and horrified*): For shame, Christoph, for shame—I don't know you anymore.

CHRISTOPH (*passionately*): Ulrich, please, come to the mountains with me tomorrow. All will become clear there. Come with me, Ulrich!

ULRICH: I wouldn't think of accompanying such a disgraceful deserter. Christoph, as long as you have lost your mind, ask your heart what Renate has been to you all through the war and up to now! How you longed for her, how everything you thought and did was hers alone—how you had thought and time for nothing but her.

CHRISTOPH: All that was a long time ago.

ULRICH (*without letting himself be interrupted*): We others who knew her—and sometimes sighed for her in secret—we didn't begrudge her to you. Christoph, must I tell you that she was sometimes in my dreams and that they were difficult nights in which I left her completely to you and to you alone? Do I have to tell you that I haven't looked at another girl since I saw Renate for the first time? Even with all that, Christoph, I have remained your friend and was able to face you with a clear conscience.

CHRISTOPH: Be quiet, Ulrich; I know all that, but don't go on. You don't understand what is happening. But believe me, one day you will understand—and you will be glad.

ULRICH: Yes, that's what they all say. I never would have thought it of you. There on your desk is still her—(*fiercely*) Christoph, where did you put her picture? Tell me!

CHRISTOPH (*softly but always decisive*): I put it away—with the music—with the memories—of which I am taking leave.

ULRICH: That is the end, Christoph. That is madness; I am going. (*Quickly walks to the door. At the same moment Renate enters.*) Renate! Sorry, Renate, I was just coming to tell you. Christoph doesn't feel well today. His wounds seem to hurt him again. He would like to be alone. It's better that we leave. (*Renate calmly walks on toward Christoph.*) No, you mustn't stay here today. It isn't good for him. He needs rest.

RENATE (*next to Christoph very quietly and lovingly*): Am I disturbing your rest, Christoph?

CHRISTOPH (*has risen, takes Renate's hand*): Stay here, Renate.

(*Ulrich exits. Renate sits down, Christoph paces the room for a while.*)

RENATE: I came to ask your forgiveness.

CHRISTOPH: You—my . . . forgiveness?

RENATE: Yes, I said the wrong things to you last night. Seeing you again after such a long time, I was so happy that I forgot what you had been through. It didn't occur to me that all of that must have changed you. I was only happy to see you. So I talked as I used to. That wasn't right. That had to hurt you. It's obvious after all that you are not the same as you were four years ago. I should have known that.

CHRISTOPH: You are good, Renate. You are always the same. Am I no longer the same? You may be right, but perhaps in a way different from what you think. Do you want me to explain it to you?

RENATE: No, Christoph, don't explain anything. That doesn't help—it only hurts. Let some time pass. Words in such instances are quite superfluous. (*In order to steer the conversation somewhere else*) What was the matter with Ulrich? He seemed upset. Excuse my asking, it's really none of my business—you needn't answer.

CHRISTOPH: I hurt Ulrich; I disappointed him. He was right, I was wrong. He had to leave.

RENATE: I don't believe that, Christoph. You can't hurt Ulrich; you can't hurt anybody.

CHRISTOPH: You are wrong, unfortunately, Renate. You are just as wrong about me as Ulrich was.

RENATE: But it's unthinkable that something should come between you and Ulrich, that you no longer understand each other, that you hurt each other.

CHRISTOPH: Not each other, Renate. I hurt Ulrich.

RENATE: Let's not argue, Christoph. I believe it, but that Ulrich breaks off with you, that he bears you a grudge I'll never believe!

CHRISTOPH: You are right, Ulrich will never do anything like that; he is much the better man of the two of us—but I, I disappointed him bitterly; so he couldn't help it.

RENATE (*sadly*): I am sorry, very sorry. Then I had better leave too. (*Slowly gets up.*)[25]

CHRISTOPH: Yes, it's better that way, I guess. You both thought too highly of me, that was the mistake. Renate, let me tell you, Ulrich is a hundred times better than I.

RENATE: Poor Christoph. Farewell! (*Exits.*)

CHRISTOPH (*paces for a while, then flings himself into an easy chair*): Yes, poor Christoph. That's what I have brought it to. Ulrich gone, Renate gone! And I wanted it this way—and now that it has come to this point I feel like a madman. That comes from wanting to be imperious when it's not really my nature. Theatrical heroism! The stranger is quite right: "Watch out, Ulrich, he is pretending to himself and the others." Why don't I do what he does and simply talk about it—as he did with Ulrich whom he didn't even know. Yes, that may be the point. I could talk with the stranger, but with Renate, with Ulrich, with my parents—that's impossible. I must go it alone. Renate, dear girl, there wasn't a thought by day or by night that didn't belong to you, no patrol that I didn't go on for you, no heat, no frost, no pain that I didn't bear for you, no piece of bread, no ray of sunshine, no flowering field in which I didn't find you, there was no note that I didn't write for you. Renate, farewell! Ulrich, you loyal friend, I trusted you blindly, you never left my side, you shared everything with me, hours of strength and of weakness.[26] I was able to tell you all, all—except for one thing. Ulrich, thank

you, I wish you happiness! (*Jumps up.*) Damned monologues —
I'll go see the stranger. (*Exits.*)

(*A short pause during which the spectators can look at details in Christoph's room. A knock at the door. No answer. The door opens, first Ulrich enters, then Renate.*)

ULRICH: He isn't here. Perhaps he went outside for a while. The fresh air will blow away his melancholy ideas.

RENATE: I think rather that he is seeking out some person.

ULRICH: What makes you think that?

RENATE: Because both of us let him down today, and now he is very much alone.

ULRICH (*somewhat upset*): He did say a while ago that he wanted to visit someone. I should have prevented that! (*Hits his hand against his head.*) Why did I run away and not stay with him?

RENATE: No, Ulrich, we must let him go completely his own way now. He won't make a bad move.

ULRICH: I guess you are right; Christoph is hardly likely to do something harmful or foolish.

RENATE: Both of us simply have to be here for him, without wanting to press or influence him. He must simply know that we are present for him.

ULRICH: No, Renate, I can't deal with Christoph in such an ethereal way. I want to know what is the matter with him. We have never kept secrets from one another up to now. He knows, too, that there is nothing he couldn't tell me, and that I would stand by him whatever it might be. But to play hide-and-seek, that I won't do. That doesn't suit Christoph or me. (*With some pathos*) That is also a betrayal of our friendship.

RENATE: Even friends, yes, even husband and wife can't always tell each other everything. They must sometimes wait for one another for a long time till the first word has grown and ripened. Words have their time. Words forced out of you are like torn-off buds. What you, with some pathos, call a betrayal of your friendship, could be just the opposite, a necessary test of your friendship.

Perhaps Christoph would betray himself and you if he said what isn't ripe yet.

ULRICH: There are no secrets between friends. Of course, people don't keep whispering to each other about all their most intimate feelings like teenage girls; one knows about them and that's it. Between friends there is openness and trust. Why else does one have a friend?

RENATE: Sometimes there are things about which one must keep silent for a while before one can say them, even among friends and between husband and wife. One must give the other time. Openness is something very beautiful, but it's even more important to be open to the other, to his silence too. And trust doesn't rest on one knowing everything about the other, but on believing in him.

ULRICH: That can be an excuse for all kinds of secretiveness, and under such a pretext much that is uncontrollable, opaque, gets between two people. I am in favor of clarity, I can't deal with imprecise matters. I want to see my friend the way he is.

RENATE: What does that mean? Do you want to see him like a photograph which registers everything, or with eyes that respectfully and lovingly perceive and receive the essential picture of the other, eyes that allow the other his secret? And what does clarity mean when often there are so many unclear things in people? One must wait for the storm to pass and the water to become clean and clear again. We must be very patient with one another.

ULRICH: Don't you know that one can miserably perish from a secret one carries around for too long and doesn't dare tell someone?

RENATE: And yet one may steal nobody's secret without destroying him. Did you never sense that especially the very good people we know carry a secret which never reveals itself and which they themselves do not dare touch? It shines through every word, through every glance of these people. But if one wanted to tell it, the best would be ruined. Good people don't know why they are that way, and they don't want to know either. The last secret of every human being is God; that we must let him have.²⁷ But actually it's nonsense, my telling you all of this. What would

Christoph be without you? You are doing everything right by yourself and — you'll go to the mountains with Christoph if he asks you, won't you?

ULRICH:[28] Don't press me, Renate, please. Do you think I could easily refuse Christoph a request? I myself could hardly bear to let Christoph go alone. Nevertheless — you don't know what stands between us. Nor could I treat Christoph as gently and patiently as you imagine. But just wait, everything will come out right again.

RENATE: I couldn't bear to see you separated. You belong together.

ULRICH: Yes, that's true, but you belong too. (*Stands at the desk and points at handwritten papers lying on the desk.*) Do you know what that is?

RENATE: No, and I don't want to.

ULRICH: But I want to show you. These are Christoph's notes[29] about his ideas which he has been discussing in our group recently. Actually nothing else has been occupying him since his return. He is completely consumed by them.[30]

RENATE: Leave it alone, Ulrich, it belongs to Christoph.

ULRICH (*laughing*): That's funny! Do you think there is a single sentence he hasn't read to me or discussed with me? It belongs to both of us. (*Picks up the papers.*)

RENATE: Please put it down.

ULRICH: No, Renate, there is really nothing in this room that doesn't belong to me as much as to Christoph. There is no secret. So listen. Because it's really good what he is writing. You'll like it. Listen to the last page he wrote.[31] (*Reads.*)

"I am speaking to you to protect from misuse the great words given to mankind. They don't belong in the mouths of the masses, or in the headlines of the newspapers, but in the hearts of the few who guard and protect them with their lives. It is never a good sign when what has always been the calm and firm possession, the unquestioned attitude, of all well-meaning people in the country is loudly hawked in the streets as the very latest wisdom. Those who are guardians of genuine values with their lives, their work, and their homes turn in disgust from the ringing rhetoric that is supposed to turn the masses into prophets. What well-meaning person can still utter the degraded words *freedom, brotherhood*, and even *Germany*? He seeks them in the quietness of the sanctuary which only the humble and faithful may approach. Each of us has risked his life for these values; those who talk about them today want to profit from them. Let us honor the great values by silence for a time, let us learn to do what is just without words for a while.[32] Then, around the quiet sanctuary of the great values, a new nobility will form in our time. Neither birth nor success will establish it, but humility, faith, and sacrifice. There is an infallible measure for the great and the small, for the valid and the inconsequential, for the genuine and the spurious, for the weighty word and the frivolous chatter—that is death. He who knows himself close to death is decisive, but he is also silent. (*Reads more and more slowly, with an expression of surprise, more to himself than to Renate.*) Without words, yes, not understood and alone if need be, he does what is necessary and just, he makes his sacrifice"—here it stops.

Strange—I didn't know this paragraph. Here is an addition in pencil: "What kind of great words are these? Why am I pussyfooting? Why don't I simply say what I mean and know? Or if I don't want to do that, why don't I keep altogether silent? How hard it is[33] to do what is necessary and what is just completely without words, without being understood. Oh, Renate! Ulrich!" (*Ulrich has read the last words with growing consternation, lowers the page, deeply moved.*) Christoph! Renate, do you understand that?
RENATE: Yes, I think so.
ULRICH: Forgive me, Renate, I didn't know. You were right. Forgive me, Christoph! Oh, God, it's impossible.
RENATE: Let it be, Ulrich, it had to happen this way. Let's go. I'll leave a note for Christoph. (*Writes something on a piece of paper. Ulrich does too; they exit silently.*)
(*Behind the door* LITTLE BROTHER's *voice*): Christoph! Christoph! Listen, it's me! (*Runs in.*) Christoph, I am allowed to go with you! I am coming to the mountains with you! (*Looks around in*

the empty room, notices the two pieces of paper and reads the first.) "Christoph, forgive me. Renate." (*Then the second one.*) "Of course I am going along, Ulrich."

(Curtain)

SCENE 3

In Heinrich's room. Bed, table, chair, sofa, picture, all in the style of a very cheap rental apartment. On the table a pistol, a bottle of schnapps and a glass, leftover food, a few pieces of paper. Heinrich restlessly paces to and fro, smoking a cigarette. The door opens softly, without a knock. Enter a middle-aged man, in the inconspicuous but correct dark clothes of an ordinary sales representative; he wears glasses that make his eyes nearly invisible; his face is totally expressionless, impenetrable, smooth like a mask.[34]

STRANGER: Good evening, young man! (*when there is no answer*) You called for me.

HEINRICH: You are mistaken. I don't know you.

STRANGER: Of course not; that's precisely why you called for me; you wanted to meet me.

HEINRICH: I told you, it's a mix-up. I am not at all in a condition to want to meet people—with one exception at best, but that's not you.

STRANGER: Who is this interesting exception, if I may ask?

HEINRICH: That's hardly your concern. So maybe you'll be kind enough[35]—(*walks toward the door*).

STRANGER: Since you won't tell me, perhaps I may be allowed to tell you. The interesting exception is a medical student of your own age, tall, intelligent, idealistic.

HEINRICH (*startled*): What do you want of me? Who are you anyway?

STRANGER: Your neighbor, sir, who watches you leave and return mornings and evenings, who sees the light in your room burn into the small hours, and who knows what is happening in this room in the lonely hours of the night.

35

HEINRICH: I seek no contact with my neighbors, especially not with curious ones.

STRANGER: *Curious* is probably an inappropriate word. I don't need to be curious.

HEINRICH: Why are you watching me then? Why are you interested in me?

STRANGER: That is part of my job, if I may say so.

HEINRICH: What is your job?

STRANGER: I can't tell you that with one word. Let's say—representative.

HEINRICH (*laughs*): Oh, and so you spied out that I lack certain requisites of middle-class life, and you want to peddle them here. It would have been better to take a closer look at my wallet. What are you selling? Oriental rugs, British fabrics, Parisian perfumes, American cars—

STRANGER: You misunderstand me, sir.

HEINRICH: Or maybe you are selling life insurance?

STRANGER: Quite the opposite.

HEINRICH: That is the first interesting thing you have said. The opposite of life insurance! Would you please explain? Here, have some schnapps. (*Both sit down.*) Tell me, which firm do you represent?

STRANGER: The most widespread and influential firm on earth.

HEINRICH: And that is . . . ?

STRANGER: Death.[36]

HEINRICH: Man, are you crazy?

STRANGER: Please keep calm, sir, and be assured that I am completely sane. I'll explain if you wish, and I am certain you'll understand me well, perfectly well, sir!

HEINRICH:[37] Yes, I won't deny that under the circumstances I am interested in your occupation. But you'll have to permit me a few questions. Yes, I am interested in your occupation—perhaps more than you suspect.

STRANGER: I know.

HEINRICH: Well, I guess the most essential questions would be: How did you get this commission? What does it pay? And who are your customers?

STRANGER: Intelligent questions—I can see we'll get on well together. How did I get my commission? Permit me to ask you a question first which will greatly promote understanding: Have you ever been condemned to death?

HEINRICH (*hesitating*): No—yes!

STRANGER: No! You once believed yourself condemned to death when you went to war. You condemned yourself to death. That is quite different.

HEINRICH (*darkly*): God had condemned me to death, but the people tricked God.

STRANGER (*with a start*): Nonsense, nothing but nonsense. You took something into your head, you were tired of life, you thought you could order Death around. You underestimated Death. It didn't come.

HEINRICH: Death will come when I want it. Here! (*Takes up the pistol.*)

STRANGER: A mistake, a dangerous mistake, if you stick to that. You can't shoot until Death permits it. Not a moment sooner. Haven't you had that thing in your hand sometimes, wanting to pull the trigger—but it didn't work, you couldn't, something— you yourself didn't know what—held on to your index finger? Don't say it was your cowardice, your thirst for life. You are not cowardly, you are not thirsty for life. It was Death.

HEINRICH: Death is an event like war, thunderstorm, earthquake. These events are in the hand of—God.

STRANGER (*with another start*): Wrong, completely wrong, you still have a great deal to learn, sir. Death is no event, it is a—being, a—lord—*the* lord. So, to make it short: I was condemned to death—not guilty of course, by the way, but that's irrelevant here. For four weeks I was staring straight at Death. At first, quite beside myself, as into a dark night when it stands before you like an impenetrable blackness, then terrified as at a falling axe, later with burning desire as for a bride on the eve of the wedding, now full of admiration as at a mighty master. When I was released, it was too late. I could no longer return to life. I had already made an agreement with Death.

HEINRICH: What does that mean?

37

STRANGER: What does it mean? I'll tell you. You see my glasses. I wear them because people told me they couldn't bear my glance since I got out of prison, that is, since I stared at Death. Since then I see all things through the eyes of Death, and you'll understand that the way Death sees everything is different from the way a living person sees.

HEINRICH: As far as I can see, you are still a living person.

STRANGER: As far as you can see, yes. But you still see very little. I know you already see much more than other people. For example, you see death in the eyes of the young medical student —

HEINRICH: Don't talk about that.

STRANGER: As you wish! I was speaking of my condemnation. At that time I learned that Death is no event, as you put it.[38] Only those who don't really know him could say that, those who have not been alone with him for days and nights. One night Death began to talk with me. I must tell you, he had a very calm, even pleasant demeanor and way of speaking. He didn't frighten me at all—there was nothing of the skeleton, hair standing on end or palms sweating from fear. No, there was something quite soothing about him. I tell you, Death is a gentleman. He demands nothing unfair, he is considerate, discreet, and he is very restrained. We had a long talk. At that time we came to an agreement.

HEINRICH: Madness!

STRANGER: Only when I was free again did I notice what had happened to me. Compared to before, people and things looked quite different. I couldn't speak to people without seeing Death standing behind them. Every one of their words seemed hollow, every laugh stale; their anger and their joy seemed meaningless. In their eyes I read—without wanting to, without doing anything about it—the time and circumstances of their demise. I saw my fiancée and immediately dissolved our relationship. My mother embraced me; I pulled back, and it was the only time since then that I felt something like tears in my eyes.

HEINRICH: Awful![39]

STRANGER: Not as awful as you think. It left me quite detached from everything. Nothing could excite me, upset me; on the contrary, I felt as calm, as empty, as solemn, and as indifferent as one does in a strange cemetery. I really feel perfectly well. No more passions, no stirrings of the heart, no hot blood—the heart ticks as regularly as clockwork—no love, no friendship, no sympathy, no tears. But I am more interested in people than ever before, since I see how Death is looking over everyone's shoulder.

HEINRICH: So you are saying that you have second sight?

STRANGER: Yes and no, for I have lost the first; I only have the "second" left. Therefore I don't suffer from it like those who are only occasionally overcome and frightened by second sight. You see, that is the point—one makes a clean sweep, one creates a simple situation. "No man can serve two masters."[40]

HEINRICH: Rather a monotonous service you are talking about.

STRANGER: On the contrary, young man, quite the contrary, it's quite diverse and varied. After all, it's not the result that's interesting, what people call death because that's the only time they see it. What is interesting is Death's slow but certain work on the living; it's the dissolution that's interesting, the decay, disintegration, and decomposition of the living body. It's dying that is interesting, not being dead; and dying lasts a long time and is just as varied as life.

HEINRICH: This conversation is beginning to disgust me.

STRANGER: I believe it, young man, and I'll tell you why. You are one of the half-people, the wounded, the weak. Sure, you know more than most—that's why I came to you—but you are making a grave mistake: You're a split personality. You see your death—fine, that's a beginning. But then you suddenly take with deadly seriousness everything you do and think; you begin to struggle, writhe, protest. You feel insulted that death is different from the way you pictured it, you reproach it for avoiding you when you were searching it out and for searching you out now that you are avoiding it. You make a grand play with the revolver, philosophize about which would be the "most honorable departure" for you; you would like Death to tickle your vanity a bit, so it goes back and forth in you and you get nowhere. You want to serve two masters, you serve neither, and you collect a thrashing from both! It's a shame about you! You are dishonest! Now your friend, this young medical student, is a very different fellow.

HEINRICH: I tell you, be quiet. If you are unhappy and have to make other people unhappy, at least you can leave me out of it — and that other fellow whom I don't know!

STRANGER: I sincerely regret having to contradict you again. I am not unhappy — I told you that before — nor do I make people unhappy. On the contrary, quite the contrary![41] What do people want? Admittedly, there were times when they wanted to live, live under any circumstances, when they turned Death into the skeleton with a scythe, when they mocked and blasphemed him; they wanted to live forever. So they created orders and laws which had no other purpose than to preserve life; whoever transgressed these orders and laws was condemned to death so that the others could live. I openly admit I have difficulty imagining myself in those times, I don't understand them. That is because I have lost my "first sight." But today? Who still wants to live? A few lovers who fear the world might collapse before they consummate their love; a few fools who get drunk with power and build themselves monuments to endure the centuries. But all the others? Who among them still blasphemes or mocks Death? Don't they rather blaspheme and mock life? I once opened the Bible in prison and read the words, "They summon death to them."[42] That's an intelligent saying. That's the way people are today. They don't fear Death, they don't flee from it, but they seek it, love it, "summon it to them." Nowadays you can make people happy only by helping them find Death.

HEINRICH: Did you ever hear that people are healthier today and live longer than they used to?

STRANGER: Quite right. But you must understand that correctly. The tactics of Death have changed with the times. Formerly, when people loved life and feared Death, it came suddenly, abruptly, horribly; it tore babies from their mothers and young mothers from their children, destroyed in a few days whole villages with epidemics and all sorts of other devastations. Today, when Death is desired, it comes slowly, creeping, with gradual, hardly perceptible dissolution. Formerly people took their lives with dagger or rope, today they take sleeping pills. Formerly people would struggle with death for days, today they go to sleep with morphine. You see, Death adapts itself. In barbaric times, when it is above all a question of life, Death too is barbaric. In civilized times when people have become honest and intelligent, Death too meets them in a civilized fashion—always, of course, *cum grano salis.* I am saying this only to prove to you that I am not making people unhappy but happy.

HEINRICH: It is a strange mixture of sense and madness you are serving up to me. Don't you see how people today try with all their might to win their right to life, joy, respect, and freedom? Isn't that a will to live that throws all your theories overboard?

STRANGER: Now you're getting to the main point; and I suppose you'll be surprised if I tell you that I myself actively support these various efforts, indeed, that this is actually my main occupation. I am working as a functionary in many of these organizations, partly from idealism, partly for business.

HEINRICH: You must get an income somewhere, and I was just wondering what you actually manage to live on.

STRANGER: Oh, don't worry about that, young man. I'll tell you in confidence, death isn't a bad business. I advise according to the circumstances: life insurance for example—some I caution against it, others I urge to take it out. I am not unknown in marriage bureaus and have helped many to a nice, easily come-by inheritance; in addition, a little of the occult; everywhere just enough for me to have what I need. But that is only—let's say— the material—

HEINRICH: Let's say the dirty side of the matter.

STRANGER: You are very stern, young man. Everyone makes his money according to his abilities. But let's get back to the main point, to the striving of the masses for freedom, equal rights, enjoyment of life, and so on. I welcome it completely and promote it. I am interested in it as in every process of dissolution and decay. People have finally become sensible; they want nothing but what is waiting for them anyhow, their death.[43] They destroy the orders and laws which kept them alive by coercion. Every servant wanting to be free of his master, every wife wanting to be free of her husband, every child wanting to be free of its parents, and all of them trumpeting that in the streets—they

41

work wholly for me, if I may put it this way. Every lazy and stupid person who wants to have the same rights as the hardworking and intelligent does so also. Everyone who arranges his life for the greatest possible pleasure does his part to accelerate the dissolution.[44] Those barbaric times when people wanted above all to live could preserve life only with the strictest laws and the severest discipline. One can really hardly think of it without a smile. People wanted to live, and what did life consist of? Work, obedience, submission, renunciation, deprivation, trouble, and effort, so that they called it a vale of tears. Everyone lived only for the other, the parents for the children, the children so that one day they too would be parents, the authorities for the subjects and the subjects for the authorities, one generation for the next and that one for the following, but no one — this is the folly of it — lived simply and honestly for himself. Nevertheless, they loved life and called the whole thing — God's commandment. What's more, they were happy in their fashion. Today, in these civilized times, people have gone beyond this kind of happiness.[45] Today people don't care anymore for life. Did they choose it? Who obliges them to live? Today they know that the greater happiness, yes, the only real enjoyment, is the dissolution of life. Marriage, family, authority, order, law — those are only relics from barbaric times that willfully clung to life. Today people die with gusto. I love the sweet smell of decay. I tell you, it's an incomparable time for people like us. One only has to recognize it and know how to exploit it. Do you understand me, young man? Come work with me. You'll get pleasure from it and make a living. (*There is a knock at the door.*) I am leaving. I only hope that your next visitor doesn't turn your head again. I bid you farewell. Good evening!

(*As he exits, Christoph enters.*)

HEINRICH (*stands in the room in confusion; shakes himself and says to himself*): Revolting!
CHRISTOPH (*stands by the door for a while, looks at the departing*

42

stranger, then says to himself): A shady character! (*turns to Heinrich, who is still motionless, and says formally, with some embarrassment*): Good evening!

HEINRICH (*the same way*): Good evening!

CHRISTOPH: I don't want to disturb you.

HEINRICH: It's all right.

CHRISTOPH (*still somewhat troubled*): Who was that?

HEINRICH: A stranger, an apparition of the night, a jailbird, a madman, a poisoner, a wild demagogue, a foul stench of carrion and corpses. He came unannounced. I didn't know him. He talked and talked at me. I sat there like a stupid little boy and couldn't find a word to say.

CHRISTOPH: What did he talk about?

HEINRICH (*looks at Christoph for the first time, calmly and firmly*): About *our* topic. Come here, sit down and have a drink!

CHRISTOPH: You aren't surprised that I came?

HEINRICH: No, I knew you would. One of us had to make the first move, and because you are the aristocrat, you came first.

CHRISTOPH: What is that supposed to mean?

HEINRICH: Very simple.[46] It didn't enter your head that you might lower yourself by coming first. People like us wonder a hundred times beforehand what kind of impression it makes,[47] how it looks, whether it won't be misunderstood. You don't need to, you are much too sure of yourself for that. You simply come, and take it for granted the other will somehow put up with it; and if he does misunderstand, that doesn't bother you at all. That's the way you aristocrats are. We others are more distrustful—and we have our experiences. But after all, we don't know each other yet.

CHRISTOPH: That's exactly why I am here. We must get to know each other.

HEINRICH: You are all enviably blind! And you don't worry what the other might think of you.[48] Perhaps the other doesn't want to meet you; but you don't care, you don't consider that possible. You don't notice that your self-assurance is essentially an unbounded contempt for people, and at that, you walk around with such modesty and calm in order to disarm us entirely. And you are even right about that, for we quietly let you feel contempt for us and are even proud of it.

CHRISTOPH: What you are saying isn't you. It's a stranger's voice.

HEINRICH: Yes, it's strange to you, but not to me. It's the voice of the common people for whom you have so much contempt. It is good for you to hear it for once.

CHRISTOPH: I have also spent four years in the trenches, just as you did. Do you really think this voice is a new one for me? I know it well enough. But because it stems from false distrust there is an impure, false tone to it; therefore it's a bad voice. I didn't come to hear this voice which isn't yours, but to talk with you man to man.

HEINRICH: Man to man[49] — you always say that when you want to silence the voice of the masses, of the common people, that lives in us. You dislike this voice; you want to rip us out of the community in which alone we are something, and you know perfectly well that you needn't fear us any longer once you confront us as individuals. As individuals we are completely powerless in your hands — for we aren't individuals, we are the masses or nothing. Man to man? Let us become men first, then we'll talk with you man to man.[50]

CHRISTOPH (*after a while, reflectively*): If a man feels contempt for himself, then he thinks all others despise him too. Heinrich, let me be frank with you.[51] As far as I know, our lives have been very different. I don't want to say that that is insignificant. I hardly know the world you grew up in; people like us never get to know it thoroughly. But you don't know my world either. I come from a so-called good family, that is, from an old, distinguished, upper-middle-class family,[52] and I am not one of those who are ashamed to admit to it. On the contrary, I know what kind of quiet strength there is in a good patrician home. No one can know that who didn't grow up in it. Also, it is hard to explain. But you must know one thing: we grew up with respect for what has developed and what is given, and so with respect for every human being. We hold mistrust to be vulgar and low. We look for the unselfconscious word and spontaneous deed

44

of the other man, and we want to accept it without suspicion. Nothing is more destructive of life together than to suspect a person's spontaneity and to be suspicious of his motives. The now fashionable psychologizing and analyzing of people means the destruction of all trust, the public defamation of all that is decent, the revolt of all that is vulgar against what is free and genuine. Men don't exist to look into the depths of each other's hearts—they are incapable of that anyway—but they should encounter each other and accept the other as he is, simply, unselfconsciously, with courageous trust. Do you understand me?

HEINRICH: I am trying to, but it is hard. Where shall I get this trust? What should I base it on? Don't you think we would also like to be able to live trusting people? Do you think we are comfortable with our perpetual suspicion? But that is precisely our trouble, that we can't afford to have trust. Our experiences are too bitter.

CHRISTOPH: A man's experiences are usually like the man himself. The distrustful person will never experience trust. Trust is always a leap over all good and bad experiences. But it may be that this leap is harder for you than for me. Therefore I came to you and didn't wait for you. You needn't think, however, that we trust blindly and that we throw ourselves into everybody's arms right away. We leave that to those who babble about the equality and goodness of everybody. We have learned to differentiate—and we'll let no one forbid us to do so—to differentiate between the genuine and the spurious, the truth and the lie, the noble and the common, the decent and the low.

HEINRICH: And what you call genuine, true, noble, decent is for you something you don't question, something self-evident, isn't it?

CHRISTOPH: There have to be self-evident things in life, and one must have the courage to uphold them. One can't begin life anew every day by calling into question again what was learned and gained the day before. Many generations have tested the things we take for granted, they have proven themselves in life hundreds and thousands of times.

HEINRICH: Yes, in the lives of your grandfathers—but times change.

CHRISTOPH: But people don't change, at least not in their essential relations. That is just the great mistake that people are always making today. They act as if the world began with them, they question everything and so never get around to contributing the small brick that is theirs to contribute to the structure of the whole.

HEINRICH: What good are bricks when the foundation has cracked?

CHRISTOPH: You talk like a journalist, and yet you know better. Were the foundation really cracked, you would be wasting your time trying to lay it again. After a thousand years of history no nation can build its foundation for the second time. If the foundation cracks, it's simply the end. But that's not the case. The foundation is deep and firm and good. One must build only on it and not beside it, on the quicksand of so-called new ideas.

HEINRICH: You mustn't believe that we are interested in new ideas, like the literati who make their profit from them. Of what concern are they to us? Truly we have neither desire nor time to hunt for originality at any price.[53] We want something much simpler: ground under our feet, so that we can live.[54] That is what I called the foundation. Don't you feel the difference? You have a foundation, you have ground under your feet, you have a place in the world; for you there are self-evident values which you can uphold and give your lives for, because you know your roots to be so deep that they'll make new growth. For you there is only one thing, to keep your feet on the ground. Otherwise you'd be like the giant Antaeus who[55] got his strength from the contact of his feet with the ground and lost it when Hercules lifted him up in battle. To be sure, there are blockheads among you too who, on their own, leave the ground on which they grew, from curiosity or vanity or because they foolishly think[56] to win us over by that. Chaff blown away by the wind. If one wants to live, there must be ground under one's feet — and we don't have this ground. Therefore we are blown about, hither and yon, by the storm. Therefore we have nothing for which we can and will give our lives. Therefore we cling to our miserable lives, not because we love them but because they are the only things we have. And if, then, death sits in your breast in the shape of a piece of shrapnel,[57] grinning at you every day — and you don't know for what purpose you are alive and for what purpose you are dying—yes, then it's a miracle if you don't go mad with the urge to live and with despair, with hatred of all that lives, and with craving for wild pleasure. Give me ground under my feet, give me the Archimedean point to stand on—and all would be different.

CHRISTOPH (*has become very pensive*): Ground under your feet— I have never understood it like that. I believe you are right. I understand—ground under your feet, to be able to live and to die.

HEINRICH: Last night you spoke very proud words about the rabble, and I agree with you. There is a rabble, and this rabble must be kept down. But what fault have those who have been pushed out into life without having been given ground under their feet? Can you walk by them and talk past them without pity?

Novel

SUNDAY

It was a hot July day in a medium-sized town in northern Germany. The sun that had risen in the cloudless sky burned hot above the suburban street as Frau Karoline Brake[1] walked home from church. The old lady somewhat wearily sat down on a bench in the park. She opened her gray silk umbrella and a little smile appeared around her eyes as she looked at the rhododendrons in full bloom. Forty years had passed since she had repeatedly begged her husband, who as the mayor[2] had something to say in these matters, to have this garden planted. She had then helped to realize the project by collecting contributions from fellow citizens and by personally donating not inconsiderable sums. For years then she was a member of the small committee that discussed and decided upon all the details of the landscaping. She had always had very definite views, and she knew how to make them prevail. So she insisted that the elderly were to have a quiet place for themselves where raucous children's games would not disturb them. And the children too should have their playground where they would not be kept from being happy and carefree by the grumpy faces and regulations of elderly people, just as the elderly should not be exposed to possible disrespect or naughtiness by the children. Above all, however — and on this point Frau Karoline Brake was inexorable — there was to be no noise in the park on Sundays. Usually Frau Karoline did not think much of signs put up by the police, but Sunday was a special matter.[3] On this day, people had to be compelled to face again the happiness that they had so carelessly discarded. The thoughtless and foolish way in which most people bypassed[4] this inexhaustible source of happiness which began anew for them each week — yes, Frau Brake said,[5] this kindest of the Ten Commandments of God — seemed as incomprehensible to the old lady now as it had then, and in that she saw one of the main reasons for the dissolution of all order, as was happening now for everyone to see. Certainly not everything was won by having outward quietness on Sundays, but that was, nonetheless, the essential prerequisite for all else. In undisguised horror Frau Karoline had watched, that very morning, how some young people had departed for the outdoors with a gramophone. What kind of enjoyment could it be that would thrive in that unnatural noise? Would these same young people not return by evening exhausted and weakened from false enjoyment? Why were human beings so afraid of silence? Was it true, as one of her grandsons had said to her recently, that the hammering and stamping of machines, the busy life in offices, and the babble of voices in a metropolis turn, when there is complete silence, into a deafening, unbearable din from which one can save oneself only with a "gentle transition"? Those were his words. People today, he said, seek and need not silence but diversion, not composure but distraction, not restraint but escape on Sundays.

Frau Karoline was sitting erect on the uncomfortable park bench, her gaze lost in the red splendor of the blooms and the dark green foliage. A few yellow butterflies soundlessly hovered in the shimmering sunny air. The gentle rustling of the birds in the bushes, their voices nearly stilled in the approaching heat of high noon,[6] the chirping[7] of the crickets, the fine high hum of the mosquitoes came to her ears through the silence in the park. Happily and with a sense of gratitude she breathed the heavy air of summer. Suddenly a shadow crossed her face. She had heard yet another miserable sermon. She had left the church in a bad mood, and only the radiant blue of the sky and nature in its summer glory had made her feel good again. The nonsense she had been subjected to! Could one blame her children and grandchildren for always letting her go to church alone?

She could still hear the cheeky words of her oldest grandson the last time he had accompanied her to church. "You know, Grandma, we have really outgrown this preacher wisdom, just like the 'Ostermann'[8] wisdom of our Latin teacher. I really don't understand how you can listen to it Sunday after Sunday."

At the time she had answered, "Dear boy, it isn't important that

50

something is new, but that it is right; and one must hear the right thing again and again because, unfortunately, one forgets it again and again."

"I don't understand," he had replied. "I don't forget it at all. On the contrary, I know all these sayings by heart."

"Yes, with your head and mouth, but heart and hand are slower to learn."

That was what she had said, but not with a completely clear conscience. For what she had heard in the sermon had been neither new nor right.[9] It was nonsense, and for her that was the worst thing there could be from the pulpit. Maybe she should have admitted that to her grandson. Maybe she should have told him, "You must not confuse Christianity with its miserable representatives."

But he was an intelligent boy and would certainly have answered, "Something that has such miserable representatives can't have much strength left. I am interested in the living and the modern, not in a past, dead belief."

How could one answer that? This distinction between the original Christianity and the contemporary church was really a way of skirting the issue. After all, it simply came down to this: whether or not Christianity, in which Frau Brake had grown up and lived her life, really was something today, including in its representatives. Every bad sermon was a nail in the coffin of the Christian faith. One could not deny it anymore: Here in this suburb, at least, the word of God had turned into nonsense. Frau Karoline Brake no longer saw the blooming shrubs, nor did she feel the good July sun; instead she saw her children and grandchildren before her and softly said, "Oh yes!"[10] and in those words there was a little surprise about the course of the world, a little sorrow about her own inability to change it in some way, but also a good deal of that calm confidence with which old people entrust the future to stronger hands.

But as if having gone too far with this little sigh, Frau Karoline sat up with a quick, somewhat vexed motion, rose, and walked with determination through the park toward the street that would lead her home. No, she wasn't one of those who capitulated prematurely! One could have seen from her walk that she was engaged in making decisions. She would see to it that this old sweet-talker disappeared from the pulpit, or else that a second minister, a preacher of the word of God, was engaged. She dismissed the idea of first speaking once more to that babbler. She had tried to several times but, as expected, had met nothing but vain hyper-sensitivity and a hollow sense of office. Yes, ever since her visit, she had felt how the minister had been avoiding her glance; and she had heard that he was agitating against her reelection to the church board by stressing with some a necessary concern about her age, with others her eccentricity, with yet others her intolerable arrogance. There was no doubt: He was afraid of her because she saw through him.[11] Despite these occurrences, she had continued going to his church on Sundays even after she lost all hope of hear-ing the word of God from him. She had accepted this humiliation as a salutary discipline.[12] But at last she could tolerate it no more. It wasn't for her personally; she had learned during the years how to ignore the babble and to hold on to the few words containing truth; she could have done that for the rest of her life. But more important things were at stake.

The congregation, the whole town, her own family were left without the word of God, and that meant, sooner or later, that all of life had to lose its orientation. This might remain hidden for a while, even though for some time memory and tradition could delay complete dissolution.[13] Already her grandchildren's genera-tion was again forced to seek its own way, and the grandmother had recognized the first signs of rebellion, yes, revolt, in several utterances of these growing children. It wasn't the fault of the young that matters stood this way, but that the adults let things go with such lack of insight and concern, that was the worst. Frau Karoline Brake had quietly wondered sometimes whether it was God's will to bring his judgment to this generation by withdrawing his word from it. But even if that was so, she told herself, then God at the same time wished people to resist this judgment, to take him by his word and not let go until he blessed them.

But why was she so alone in her thoughts and views? Why was it that of those who were in church today, hardly anybody except the old sexton noticed that they heard nothing but empty declamations and cheap phrases? Why did the educated people, especially, fail so completely in their judgment? Of course, they hardly ever went to church, but if they had to go to a baptism or a wedding then they always thought the speech—that's what they called the sermon—very nice, very artistic, very modern, very relevant. The old woman[14] shook her head in vexation and was deep in thought when she heard a voice behind her: "Good morning, my dear Frau Brake,[15] hasn't God given us another wonderful day?"

It was the neighbor, Director Warmblut's widow, who was also coming from church and, after having talked to two or three other ladies of the suburb on the way home, had now energetically hurried after Frau Karoline Brake to reach her before they got to their houses. It had been hard for this little, somewhat rotund woman to catch up with her neighbor, who was ten years her senior; and now, with a very red, shiny face, and a bit out of breath, she was hurrying next to the vigorous and stately figure who, in her gray dress, with her gray silk umbrella, her gray hair and the dry, gray skin of her intelligent face, presented a rare picture of sedateness and dignity.

"Good morning," said Frau Brake in her quiet, clear voice, "yes, the sun does us good; we need it too."

"Oh, I do hope you are well. What wonderful health God has given you! Oh well, he loves you, how could it be otherwise? Such a blessed family life, and the beloved grandmother the idol of her grandchildren. Oh, those charming children—though they're growing up more and more now. But they stay good; yet, coming from the old mold, how could it be otherwise? What happiness for you, so completely in the circle of your family! Just imagine, my dear Frau Brake, I have had such problems again in the last few days. Oh, I know, the greater the cross, the nearer is heaven. How could it be otherwise? But imagine, my daughter Hilde's husband has canceled his church membership and doesn't want the baby baptized. I cried and cried about it. What would my late husband have said? What will people think of us? And what shall become of the poor girl? Yes, and I am almost ashamed to say it, my Hilde doesn't take it badly at all; the child can later decide herself what she wants, Hilde says. Oh, that hurt me so much, that this should happen with my own children! And all of that with the position my late husband occupied. I can't understand it. I have always told her about God and prayed with her. She always went with me to the minister at the church. At the wedding he gave my Hilde such beautiful rules of conduct, and the motto 'Do right and fear no one' always hung over her bed. Believe me, my dearest Frau Brake, I haven't been able to sleep for several nights from worrying about my child. But today during the sermon everything went away, and now I am quite relieved and happy. Oh, that the dear Lord has given us our dear church and also our dear minister who can make such human, relevant, and beautiful speeches! Forgive me; I know, Frau Brake, you don't always agree with him—but today, you must admit, today he surpassed himself.''

"Yes, today he really surpassed himself, Frau Warmblut.''

"You see, you see, oh, how glad I am that you agree. Didn't he say it beautifully? Yes—what did he say, actually? It's impossible to repeat it, but it doesn't matter, one can feel it and one is quite uplifted and doesn't really know why, isn't that right, dearest Frau Brake?''

"Yes, one really doesn't know why.''

"At any rate he said that everyone should live the way he thinks right, and then it is right; and it doesn't really much matter to God whether or not the child is baptized—isn't that right, Frau Brake—and whether or not my little Hilde goes to church, that doesn't actually matter much. After all, we are free people—that's how he expressed himself. Oh, how wonderful, this idea! So liberating, so profound—how could it be otherwise, don't you think, dearest Frau Brake? He also had a biblical text. Now what was the connection?''

"Yes, what was the connection, Frau Warmblut?''

"Yes, what was it? Oh—you are confusing me, Frau Brake. But it doesn't matter, does it?''

"No, it really doesn't matter, for there wasn't any connection.[16] He wanted to preach about plucking the corn on the Sabbath Day and about the text 'The Son of man is Lord even of the Sabbath.'[17] And instead of saying that what Christ is permitted to do because he is Christ we are not permitted to do by a long shot, and that when Christ keeps the Sabbath by profaning it, then we must first learn to keep the day of rest really holy by observing it—instead, he babbled about the freedom of all men, and that everyone is permitted to do what he thinks right, and that on Sundays one should rather go into the outdoors than to church, and that it doesn't really matter anyway because the dear Lord is so good, so dear and nice that he can't get angry at all. Dear Frau Warmblut, didn't you notice that the minister preached what the congregation wanted to hear, but not the word of God?''

Frau Karoline Brake had arrived at the garden gate of her children's house. She at once firmly pressed the bell and, when the door opened, turned once more to her companion. She thought, Did it make sense to deprive this foolish, loquacious woman of her happiness? Do I have the right to criticize the sermon she found so beautiful? Am I called upon to scare this self-satisfied woman out of her peace? Is there anything at all one can do to combat this shallowness? Again—who can see into another's heart? "Man looketh on the outward appearance, but the Lord looketh on the heart.''[18] And yet—this pious chatter no longer has anything to do with Christianity; it is more dangerous than outright disbelief. These thoughts went quickly through Frau Karoline's head and for a moment robbed her of the assurance she rarely lost otherwise.

"Farewell, dear Frau Warmblut," she said more warmly than before; "and you know—perhaps your daughter is quite right. Good bye!''

"But dear Frau Brake, now I don't understand you at all any more; I am completely mixed up. Little Hilde is supposed to be right? No, you can't be serious. You are usually so strict in these matters. Oh no, you're joking. How charming of you, this golden sense of humor! What a pity we are home already. I do enjoy chatting with you. But I mustn't keep you; the dear family is waiting. Farewell again. It was another wonderful morning, wasn't it? Good-bye, farewell, dear Frau Brake! I have got to think some more about what you said.''

Frau Brake closed the gate, and a slight pity touched her when she looked into the disappointed, good-natured face of her neighbor. Yes, do think about it, she said to herself, but it's not likely to help much, she added with a quick smile. Then her face suddenly assumed the expression of great dissatisfaction with herself. "I have done it wrong again; it's just too difficult," she thought.

The maid appeared at the door and relieved Frau Brake of her umbrella. "Good morning, Elfriede," said Frau Brake, "didn't I see you in church today? You get home faster than I. How are you?"

"Oh, madam, it was so beautiful and solemn in church again. And when I think of the minister, how he feels really at home in the pulpit, how he speaks so loudly and clearly in his deep voice and then leans across the pulpit and reaches out with his arms—that always goes to one's heart—and that he knows all the worries people of our kind have; he wouldn't need to, such a fine gentleman as he is. In our village the minister was so different, he always spoke evenly and only about the Bible and so on—no, if one compares, one realizes that one is living in a suburb of the big town. One always feels quite uplifted when one comes from church here."

"Go, Elfriede," said Frau Brake, "and before dinner, read this Sunday's text once more; that will be good for you. Are the master and mistress at home?"

"The professor was working in his room until a little while ago, and madam was checking the young people's clothes. A few minutes ago the master and mistress went out with their tennis rackets. I was to tell madam that they'll be back at one o'clock sharp."

"All right, child,[19] you may go now—Wait, just a moment! Can't you remember, Elfriede, where my things go? Again and again you hang them on the professor's hook—you can read, can't you! It says clearly above each hook,[20] 'Father, Mother, Grandmother.' Remember now!"

Embarrassed, Elfriede quickly took Frau Brake's hat and umbrella, hung them in their place, and disappeared. Briefly and with a visible expression of satisfaction, the grandmother glanced at the big clothes stand which, with its long row of hooks, completely occupied the one wall of the spacious front hall. In the father's spot there was only the walking stick with the simple silver handle, an heirloom from his father; on the mother's hook hung the white silk scarf,[21] as light as a feather, which her husband often put around her in the garden on a summer evening; then came the grandmother, and after her the long row of the children.

On the hook of the oldest son, Franz, hung a very well worn hat, and on it, although the mother had spoken out against it a hundred times, were two books: Feuerbach's *Lectures on the Essence of Religion*[22] and an English book about the labor movement. For weeks now Franz had been carrying these books around with him and would not be parted from them.[23] One Saturday evening when the family had gathered to make music, during a trio played by his young brothers and sisters Franz took a volume out of his pocket and began to read; the father forbade it firmly but kindly. Franz[24] remonstrated in reply, in a manner never heard before: He declared that one had to make better use of one's time nowadays than to hold traditional family gatherings without any point to them; that one couldn't expect him to allow the musical amateurism of his brothers and sisters to disturb his work; moreover, that it was wrong to cultivate musical productions artificially when there was no talent; and that one would do better to put all that money at the disposal of really gifted members of the working class for their training. A deathly hush fell over the room during this extraordinary incident. The father answered unusually sharply that he was still the father of the family and, once and for all, refused to tolerate his son's criticism of the way he disposed of his money. Moreover, it was quite superfluous that Franz took the side of the poor against him; he knew more about that from his medical practice than Franz from his books. And as far as the family gatherings and the music were concerned, Franz would some day judge differently. Then, when the children continued their trio after a friendly glance from the father, Franz left the room, deathly pale and shaking with agitation. The grandmother had worried for a long time about the big, smoldering eyes, the pale complexion, and the fanatically set mouth of the young student. On this Sunday, it seemed, he had finally gone outside with his brothers and sisters without taking his books, perhaps a hopeful sign of some inner calm. The grandmother, who was particularly fond of this oldest grandson, took the books from the stand to put them in Franz's room and so avoid any further irritation of the parents.

On Christoph's hook hung a strange loden coat that had distinct signs of frequent use in the woods on rainy days. "Oh yes, Ulrich's, of course," said Frau Brake to herself with a smile. There followed Klara's pretty summer jacket, embroidered by her with Grandmother's patterns, and underneath a pair of dainty galoshes; then Martin's much mocked schoolcap from the junior class at the Gymnasium. "I don't see why I always have to attract attention in school; no other boy wears such crazy homemade suits and fantastic hats as I do. I don't want people always looking and laughing at me in the street." Fortunately it hadn't occurred to this boy with the unusually intelligent, clear eyes and the vivacious, ever-cheerful expression that people smiled at him not because of his[25] unusual clothes but from inner pleasure over his whole appearance. When the response of people didn't change (despite the schoolcap he got with his father's reluctant permission, though opposed by all brothers and sisters), Martin secretly worried for a while that there might indeed be something ridiculous or crazy in his personality or appearance, and so became embarrassed and timid. But since he didn't want to discuss it with either his older brothers or his parents—one didn't talk about such personal matters but came to terms with them on one's own—he had, one day, tested the ground with his grandmother by suddenly blurting out the question of whether crazy people know that they are crazy.

After the grandmother's surprised answer, that he should ask his father sometime because as a doctor he could tell him exactly, but that as far as she knew it varied, the boy had beaten around the bush for a while and finally said, "I mean, Grandma, if someone has something ridiculous in his face or his walk, or if he looks particularly dumb, does he always know that?"

Then the grandmother had known what the matter was and had patted Martin's head and said, "Dear boy, what silly ideas you have," and had looked at him so kindly and almost cheerfully that Martin had run out of the room with a beet-red face, but overjoyed.

Since then his school cap hung unworn in its place, and no one but the grandmother, who knew how to keep quiet, knew why.

Above the following hook, from which hung all sorts of children's things, it said "Little Brother." His brothers and sisters, if asked, would hardly have known that their youngest brother was actually called Ekkehard. Also they would have been ashamed to pronounce this name; it seemed "affected" and "pathetic" to them. But at his birth his mother had insisted on the name,[26] which was not her usual way; perhaps it seemed too bombastic to her in the course of time, or perhaps because of an unconscious rejection by the rest of the family—at any rate, Ekkehard was never called anything but Little Brother. And as happens with such names, it clung to the little boy in school as well. For pupils and teachers he was the Little Brother. He was, incidentally, the only one in the Brake family who wasn't called by his baptismal name; ordinarily it was almost a family principle to avoid all diminutives, pet names, and nicknames. "It is a privilege of the aristocracy and the film stars to call their children Mautz and KoKo and Piffchen," the father had casually said at table once, and as often happens, since this casual, jocular pronouncement, it was[27] settled for the children that they had no use for such silly extravaganzas—and questions of taste often quickly turn into moral judgments for young people, as we know. So they couldn't find enough fault with, and make enough fun of, the fact that the greengrocer's children were called Thekla and Armin, and they almost took credit for their own names being neither fantastic nor literary nor theatrical but sensible middle-class names, and yet not quite run-of-the-mill. But *Ekkehard*, in their collective opinion, transcended the limits of the permissible, which were as firmly maintained as they were hard to define; *Little Brother* was definitely more natural.

Where was Little Brother this morning, by the way? His things were all here. The little eight-year-old latecomer often felt neglected among his older brothers and sisters, and so when they went out, he usually preferred to stay in the garden. With a glance Frau Karoline Brake passed over the last three clothes hooks, destined for guests; on Sundays the coats of the oldest daughter, who had been married for six months, and of her husband, a senior government official, frequently hung there.

This front hall with its long wall of clothes couldn't exactly convey to guests the impression of an elegant house. Of course, one could immediately see in the bright room that the wood and metal were of heavy, first-rate quality, meticulously polished and cared for. On the parquet floor lay a thick braided rug. As long as they couldn't keep their shoes clean, the children shouldn't run across oriental rugs—that was the mother's opinion. But she didn't think it right to make the children go through the kitchen door. A few good engravings of German cities hung on the free walls of the hall.

Frau Karoline Brake opened the door and went through the wide, cool living room (fancy names like *parlor* were taboo in the family) and dining room, shaded from the sun, toward the enclosed veranda, the shades of which were down. Frau Brake felt comfortable in these great rooms. The long dining table with the simply carved but solid wooden chairs had formerly been in her house; the sideboards were old-fashioned but of good craftsmanship and design. The small antique silver dish from which the grandmother gave chocolates to her youngest grandchildren on special occasions had stood tightly closed in the same place for years, and even Martin, the fifteen-year-old, was not above being included with the little ones in this case.

On the walls hung good portraits of all four grandparents, of whom only Frau Karoline Brake was still alive. Although both grandfathers had been respected men in high offices, there was no sign on their pictures of the public honors they had enjoyed. "I am having my portrait painted for my family and not for the town hall," Grandfather Brake had said. When the older children, who were attached to these pictures, occasionally visited other homes and saw there the portraits of the heads of the house in official robes, adorned with all their decorations and medals, they simply thought it funny, at first.

Later, in an especially striking case, Christoph once emboldened himself to speak of "parvenu taste," and though his father secretly agreed with him and was glad about the sureness of his instincts, he had answered, "Dear boy, remember it isn't proper for you, at your age, to judge other people. When they kindly invite you into their house, it isn't fitting to criticize their way of living and furnishing. That is an abuse of hospitality, let me tell you. You still have to learn how good it is that people differ, and you mustn't take offense at externals. It is stupid to compare all the time and to judge everybody by one standard." A reply to the statement of his father, who was his absolute standard for everything, was out of the question for Christoph. But the pronounced instinct for quality that he possessed and shared with his father[28] became increasingly strong and conscious in him after this conversation. What was new to him was only the idea that the right feeling for quality must be coupled with patience and reserve toward people of a different kind; learning that took many years and much experience.

While the grandparents' pictures were thus an integral part of the growing children's lives, the somewhat stiffly painted picture of the great-grandfather which hung over a small corner sitting area was of special importance. At the bottom, in old-fashioned script, it said, "This is the Reverend Justus Brake, Provost of the Cathedral, who paid for the Word of God with his life and taught it with his death." The old provost was portrayed kneeling in front of an altar with Christ on the cross, holding in his hand an hourglass which had run down. This old orthodox Lutheran minister[29] was driven from his pulpit in the time of rationalism, and when he refused to leave his congregation, despite orders from the authorities that he go, he was imprisoned. Finally, through the efforts of his loyal congregation, he was released and reinstated in his office. But during his first service in his church, weakened by the long imprisonment, he had collapsed and died at the altar, with his eyes on Christ on the cross. The children had known this story since they were small, and they revered the picture of their[30] ancestor almost like a little saint's picture. Even when the older ones grew more distant from the church, this didn't change. The old minister lived as a quiet ideal in their hearts.

Aside from this special case, there was no ancestor worship in the family. The family tree of the Brakes, which hung by the stairs, belonged to the house just as naturally as all the many heirlooms in the various rooms. An old, wealthy, do-nothing uncle, who appeared from time to time and, in a resonant voice, spoke of nothing but the meritorious services of the Brakes during the last four hundred years, could barely be protected by the parents from the children's boisterous mocking.

"Uncle Theodor, do you think the world will collapse when there are no more Brakes?" the fourteen-year-old Franz had once asked with pretended naiveté.

The foolish uncle had fallen into the trap, answering, "But I am so happy, my boy, that you think so. Do think that way always, then you'll turn into a genuine Brake."

Franz, who had nearly burst out laughing, received a punishing glance from the mother. Christoph, sitting next to him, whispered into his ear, "He makes me sick!"

The children derived their greatest pleasure from the father's polite evasions of the uncle's repeated expostulations about the urgent necessity of founding a family club and archive.[31] "You are a living family club on your own, Uncle Theodor," said the father.

"But what will happen when I am dead?"

"Well, then that's the end of the Brakes in any case."

"But no, dear nephew," the uncle replied, somewhat uncertainly and flattered, "you can't be serious, or are you?"

At this moment the mother came to his aid, offering something delectable to the uncle, who was unable to resist the Brake family's cuisine, and thereby turning the conversation to other matters. This scene, with variations, had been played several times before the children, so that whenever the uncle came to visit they were waiting for this moment, kicking each other under the table when it came—and once, by mistake, the uncle himself got a strong kick on the shin and looked around with utmost astonishment but said not a word.

So it happened that the children of the Brake house pursued all "playing at family," as they called it, with grim mockery, and one could have found in them rather too little than too much sense of family. They would have preferred to address distant aunts and cousins formally—"But we don't know each other and we really have nothing to do with each other." If the mother then said, "But children, they are your father's relatives after all!" then their laughing retort was, "Mother has joined the family club!" Nevertheless, a nearly unbroken stream of visiting relatives flowed through Professor Brake's hospitable home, and Klara had once said, "I think the relatives are using Papa a bit. He is always supposed to be responsible for everything. Everyone comes to him with their petty complaints, even though Papa has more to do than any of them. Papa is too good-natured,[32] and sometimes they don't even say 'thank you.'" There was something to that; people took the generous helpfulness of the wealthy and influential professor[33] and his wife far too much for granted.[34] Frau Maria Brake had undertaken the furnishing of the house with great confidence and independence and with a liberal expenditure. Untroubled by questions of style and conventional taste, she aimed exclusively at an attractive and generous dwelling for her family, and it was surprising to see how this point of view managed to combine the old with the new, and things of great artistic value with those of value only as personal mementos, and how they formed a natural and meaningful entity together. It was not a fabricated house, but one that had grown organically. One could move in it with instinctive freedom and without inhibition. One felt drawn into the warm atmosphere of a strong family life without being crushed by it; one sensed an unobtrusive wealth and a taste for enjoyment and comfort. It was less the meaning of the individual object than the solicitous care of the whole that was pleasing to eye and heart.

Frau Karoline Brake had taken a seat on the veranda and looked out into the big garden. She had come to terms with the fact that her daughter-in-law allowed the greater part of the place to grow unchecked in order that the children could move and play there freely. Only a magnificent rose arbor, flowering in all colors, had been cultivated in front of the veranda where they had breakfast on summer days. Behind it the wilderness began, with a meadow of tall grasses in flower, thickly leaved and overgrown bushes with dark hiding places and robbers' dens, and even a small pond supplying inexhaustible material for the terrarium and microscope of the nature-loving children. With their father's help, the children had built a solid, spacious tree house in the strong branches of an old linden tree, where they ate their afternoon sandwiches with special pleasure. The garden ended with a light wooden fence, through which a gate led directly into the neighboring forest.

Among the tall grasses of the meadow and the bushes, Frau Brake saw the blue jacket of her youngest grandson appearing and disappearing,[35] and next to him the slight figure of the neighboring porter's ten-year-old son in his heavy gray Sunday suit. In the Sunday morning quiet one could hear the voices of the two children from the open veranda. Now they sat down together on a small wooden bench in front of the bushes. Little Brother put his hand into his pocket and took out a tiny piece of chocolate that had probably become quite soft in the heat, a cookie, and half an apple.

"From last night," he said, and passed these contents of his pocket to his friend.

He took it and at the same time pulled from his pocket a bag,[36] opened it, let Little Brother look in, gave it to him, and said, "I collected those yesterday after the rain—for your terrarium—look at that one!" With that he took a fat earthworm out of the bag and both boys admired it.

"Thank you, Erich," Little Brother said and put the bag into his pocket.

"And I also made you a slingshot for the cat if it tries to get at these birds' nests; you can use a pretty big stone in it," Erich said and immediately demonstrated the weapon for his friend.

Little Brother took it, and for a while the boys passed the time by taking turns shooting at a tree. There was little talk while they did that. A short time later the kitchen windows downstairs were opened, and a strong aroma of roasting meat came into the garden.

"Yummy, what a smell at your house," Erich said. "We are having cabbage and potatoes today. Do you always eat meat?"

"I don't really know," answered Little Brother, "sometimes, at any rate."

"We only eat meat once a week when my father has a day off. Today he is working."

"But it's Sunday today, Erich," said Little Brother. "Nobody works on Sunday."

"Oh yes, my father works for the railroad, they work on Sundays too and also at night."

"Also at night?" Little Brother asked with surprise. "Then when does he sleep?"

"During the day," said Erich.

"But why does he do that? Did he choose to? And how do you celebrate Christmas when your father happens to be working?" Little Brother asked.

"Last time we celebrated the day after," said Erich.

"But that isn't nice!"

"No, it isn't nice, but it couldn't be helped."

"But what if your father simply said, 'I can't work today, it's Christmas today'?"

"Then he'd lose his job."

"Well, that's fine, isn't it?"

"You are dumb, Little Brother; then we wouldn't have anything to eat."

"Oh," Little Brother said slowly and thoughtfully.

After a while he asked, "Is your family poor, Erich? Poor people are always hungry and have no clothes to wear and are cold in the winter."

"I don't know, Little Brother, I asked my mother once and she said we have just enough and must be content."[37]

"That's too bad!"

"Why?"

"Because all people have to be nice to the poor because they are poor."

"Really? I never heard that. Is your father rich, Little Brother?"

"I don't know, Erich,[38] I don't think so; because my mother never wants us to talk about money and always says 'm' instead of 'mark' and I only get ten pfennig allowance a week and you get fifty. Also we are never allowed to eat ice cream in the street, and we always take everything along from home when we go on a short trip. Are your parents saying that we are rich?"

"No, my parents have never said that yet, but other people do."

"Oh, don't worry about it, Erich, they just want to make us mad."

"What do you want to be later, Little Brother?"

"I don't know exactly what it's called, but when I grow up

I'll buy a big house and then I'll make the veranda into a great big bird cage and I'll travel everywhere, to Africa and America too, and I'll get all the birds from those places, and then we'll both feed them and watch them all the time so we'll know how they do things.''

"That's nice, but I'll also have to go to work for the railroad later.''

"Why?''

"My father said so, but I'll come visit you often.''

"Yes, of course, all day and also always on Sundays, like now. Have you got your whistle with you? Let's go to the nests in the bushes for a while.''

The two boys dug in their pockets, and each pulled out a little reed whistle made by Erich's father for imitating birdcalls. That had been their favorite entertainment for months.[39] Often the two sat very quietly near the bushes for hours on end, listening to the calls, most of which they knew, and luring the birds with quite a lot of skill. They hated all cats showing up in the vicinity and drove them away with handfuls of sand. So Frau Brake saw the two children disappear into the bushes again today.

A shrill scream made her jump. She recognized Little Brother's voice; the child wasn't visible. It wasn't usually his way to cry even when he was hurt. And it sounded less a cry for help than one of rage. Frau Brake was already on the steps to the garden and hurried toward the wilderness without being able to spot Little Brother. Then she heard soft weeping and found the boys kneeling in the bushes. Little Brother was holding a young bird.

"She pushed it out of the nest,'' he said, tears streaming down his face, when he saw the grandmother.

"Who, the cat again?''

"No, much worse; the mother herself, the bad, mean beast.''

The young bird twitched once more, then died in the boy's hand.[40] That was too much for him. Frightened, he involuntarily opened his hand and dropped the dead little robin. Then he felt shame, reached again for the little bird, stood up, and showed it to his grandmother.

"Put it under the earth," she said; "it'll feel most comfortable there."

Erich wordlessly took a big spade, pushed it deep into the soil, and Little Brother laid the bird into its grave and covered it up. The grandmother took her small grandson's hand and went to the house with him. Erich stayed for a moment and then quickly ran out to the street.[41]

"Why did the mother do that?" Little Brother asked when the grandmother came to his room with him to wash his face and get him ready for Sunday dinner.

"Probably because the young bird was weak and sick," Frau Brake answered calmly. She would have disdained using such an elemental experience as a dishonest lesson, perhaps by saying, "Because the young bird was naughty." In any case, Frau Brake considered the truth better pedagogy than subterfuges and tricks.

Little Brother was taken aback and forced to ponder by this plain answer. The tears dried up. He tried to understand, but he couldn't.

"Because the young bird was weak and sick—the mother threw it out of the nest? She doesn't nurse it?"

"No, Little Brother, with the animals only the strong and healthy can live. But with people it's different."

"But that's bad of the mother bird, simply to kill her young!"

"No, Little Brother, you mustn't say that. Animals are innocent; they have to live this way."

Little Brother shook his head. "I didn't know that; I think in that case I won't want to have a birdhouse later. Does God actually know all that, Grandmother?"

"Yes, he knows. Jesus says, 'Not one sparrow shall fall on the ground without the will of my Father.' "[42]

"Does Jesus know that for sure?"

"Yes, he knows for sure."

"So, does God also know the little bird we just buried, and[43] is it now with God?"

"Yes, God knows it; there is not one sparrow forgotten before God, Jesus says too."[44]

"Then that's good," said Little Brother.

"Yes, God's will is always good," the grandmother said.

Little Brother pondered. After a while he said, "But it's also good that with people it's different. Father helps the sick and weak people, doesn't he, Grandmother?"

"Yes, child, he tries to."

"Can't he always help them?"

"Often, but not always."

"Do they have to die then?"

"Yes, child."[45]

"And what happens then?"

"Then they stand before God and ask him to let them come to him."

"Is God very strict?"

"Yes, very strict but also very good."[46]

"Do people always know beforehand when they have to die?"

"Not always, but sometimes."

"I would like to know it beforehand; then I'd very quickly do an awful lot of good so that God would have to take me to him."

"God doesn't have to do anything, child, he does everything as he wills."

"But if one begs him very hard?"

At about the same time the young generation of the Brake family was having a noon rest by the edge of a calm lake in the forest.[47] The brothers and sister had started out at five o'clock in the morning, had taken the train part way, and had then walked for several hours to get to know a more distant area of the woods. Hikers only rarely came to these parts, and for a whole hour they hadn't met anyone. They had come along a trail through some tall, mixed woods with old trees and broad, light clearings and had followed a lively, rapidly widening brook. With a good feeling for the terrain, they had expected where the hills got lower a pond in which to refresh themselves. When they really did see water—sparkling through the trees with the sunshine on it—they had uttered little cries of joy and run down the hill to the edge of the water.

The young men had already thrown down their knapsacks and

pulled out their bathing things when Klara cried, "Wait, first we are going to hunt mushrooms for lunch, and while they are cooking we can have a dip!"

Then everyone quickly grabbed a container brought along for just this purpose, and after only half an hour a goodly amount was spread out on a bed of moss and once more submitted to a joint inspection: firm, robust cèpes, which had stood in whole families by the rarely frequented edge of the woods; light yellow chanterelles; rust-colored leccina; tall, feathered parasol mushrooms, still closed; stately, smooth tricholomae; bleeding lactarii; and a huge number of aromatic marasmii — against the dark green moss they were a colorful picture of the fruits of the forest. While Klara and Martin cleaned the mushrooms and peeled potatoes, the older ones built a safe place for the fire. In a short time the fire was crackling under the pot, and a few minutes later the youthful group was laughing, splashing, and gasping in the water. For a short time they sunbathed on a big raft which they were happily surprised to find, and then they toppled each other back into the water. While the boys were still swimming, Klara had gone on land, finished the cooking, and was now calling them for lunch. Out there in the field under the shady trees at the edge of the cooling water, the new potatoes and the fresh, aromatic mushrooms were an unsurpassed feast. They ate in silence, and with the food they also took deeply into themselves other strengths: the forest, the sun, the water, the community of brothers and sisters, the family, the homeland, freedom — all of these each of the young people more or less consciously received in this silence as a great, shared gift.

Now it was the noon rest. The hot sun reflected brightly in the water, blinding the eyes. Dragonflies were flitting across the surface and climbing up and down the reeds. The fifteen-year-old Martin, lying on the raft amid the rushes, observed for the first time in thoughtful amazement how some of them ran down the stalk, briefly disappeared in the water, and soon surfaced again. What can they be looking for in the water? What are they hiding there? How can they breathe down there? he thought. Tonight he would ask his father. When the sun was too hot on his back, he skillfully built himself a small hut of branches and with his hands slowly paddled along the edges of the pond, occasionally saw a water bird hurriedly disappear into the water when he came close, enjoyed the little leaps of the small fish, and threw back into the pond a fat frog that had climbed onto the raft. Once there was a loud noise in the rushes, and a big bird flew up with a strong flapping of its wings directly above Martin's head.

"A heron!" Martin cried, half startled and half ecstatic; then it was quiet again.

Klara had fallen into a deep sleep in the shade of a mighty beech tree. Her thick blonde hair was loosened and lay across her shoulders and breast. She was quietly and evenly breathing the summer forest air.

Franz had retired to the next clearing. He didn't want to sleep and yet wished to be quite undisturbed; so he sat on an old tree stump, a book on his knees, and to keep off the insects, he had draped an old rain cape over his bare skin. Now the world receded around him, and he saw only the starved laborers of Zola's *Germinal*.[48] "There is the real life, there are our tasks, only there is the confirmation of our lives, all else is play, dream,[49] idleness, frivolity, yes, even worse, is unscrupulousness, depravity—is thievery," he mused; "damn that I let myself be caught and lulled to sleep again and again." He knew he had to shut his eyes to his brothers and sisters if he wanted to talk like that. Had he now seen his young sister sleep so peacefully like a child of nature, had he seen his young brother watch the doings at the pond's edge with attentive eyes and mind, had he thought of the simple meal they had just shared so happily and[50] with natural unpretentiousness, then he would have had to see that life is richer and more varied than it often says in books. But now he didn't want to see and know that. Like a hermit he sat there in his odd covering, and visions of a better, more just, more beautiful world rose before him and made him glow. And what was good and beautiful in the existing world so near to him fell apart into ashes before the burning images of the future that he beheld and whose dawning he believed to have come. Whoever saw him over his books like that with his dark eyes, his

warm, not yet fanatical expression, his clear features, his good forehead, would have been strongly impressed by this twenty-year-old.
But he, of all people, who in his thoughts sought the community
of the disadvantaged and weak, had the reputation among his fellow students of being unapproachable, and among the weak and
mediocre, even of being haughty.

On an incline that rose gently from the lake and, treeless, was
exposed to the hot sun, Christoph and Ulrich lay on their backs in
the tall grass, their hands under their heads, their glances directed
now to the sky, now across the lake,[51] each with a slouch hat of gray
linen on his head. The sun couldn't do anything to their hardened,
tanned bodies. Anyone seeing the two would have thought them
brothers, as indeed happened frequently enough. Since his twelfth
year, when his mother had moved to the suburb with him and he
had joined Christoph's class, Ulrich had indeed been received like
a son in the Brake's house and like a brother by the children. It was
simply a foregone conclusion that Ulrich was part of every under-
taking, every event, every trip, and every celebration. But Christoph,[52] who in contrast to his elder brother had always felt a great
need for heart-to-heart talks and personal community, and found
his little brother too young for that, could no longer be imagined
without Ulrich.

It was one of those inseparable, unclouded, rare friendships
which make young lives rich and happy and protect them from
inner dangers and mistakes, friendships[53] that are stormily formed
in the years of unfinished and fermenting youth and that ripen in
the years of maturity to the fullness and splendor of a noble wine.
In school, at home, on countless hikes, Christoph and Ulrich got to
know each other down to the smallest detail of their behavior, their
views, their interests, abilities, and qualities. Happily, each had
discovered in the other a similarity in feeling about all essential
aspects of life, and the smallest cues in facial expression or in the
choice of words fully sufficed the two friends for complete mutual
understanding in certain situations. In spite of that, they had never
become boring to each other. For Christoph's ever vehement and
lively way of thinking, the clarity and perspicuity of Ulrich's per-

sonality had become indispensable. Ulrich, on the other hand, found in Christoph's confidence and decisiveness the support which he sought.

"This is certainly different from those miserable school trips," said Ulrich, stretching his arms and pulling his knees up.

"You didn't tell me, how were the three days in S.?" asked Christoph without turning.

"Simply awful, I tell you, I don't want to think about it here.[54] Beer gardens, card games, boasts and vulgarities; in the afternoon, promenading after the belles of the town, in long trousers of course, colorful ties, pomaded hair, but unwashed from the neck down; enough to make one sick, I tell you. In the evening, experiences in the park, and so on;[55] and the money that was thrown about, I wouldn't like to know where that came from, and the whole thing the brilliant idea of the senior-class president of a humanistic Gymnasium."

"Then why did you go along?[56] I thought right away it would be like that."

"You know, I thought so too, but my mother was all in favor of my going. She thought we held back too much from the others and that that wasn't good. When I told her you weren't going either, she said it was different for you; I couldn't afford such solitude. She simply can't get rid of the idea that I might accustom myself to a life style in your house which doesn't suit our circumstances."[57]

"Well, our so-called life style today is much less expensive even than the vacation pleasures of our fellow students, for example," Christoph laughed.

"Of course, Christoph, Mother knows that too, basically, and it is really rather the seclusion she fears for me. 'You are like a thousand others,' she said, 'and you have to accustom yourself to getting along with them. You can't spend the rest of your life with the Brakes.' If she only knew what I am supposed to become accustomed to, she wouldn't have a single minute of peace while I am at the Gymnasium. But how am I supposed to tell her? And perhaps it isn't so bad, in spite of everything, that one has seen that for once. But ugh—it was disgusting! Incidentally, they aren't all like that. It's always just the few big wheels, and then the rest topple over. Do you know, by the way, that Meyer has been kicked out?''

"Really? That's good. He was a real swine, in every respect. I wouldn't have wanted to shake hands with him."

"But that's not why he was kicked out, but because they have kept him from taking finals for the third time, because he wasn't up to them even now, before the summer vacation, which is really unusual. I know his mother; she is a seamstress and she really had to pinch every penny to be able to get her boy through Gymnasium.''

"Serves her right!''

"Christoph!''

"Well, Ulrich, am I not right? What do we get out of chasing and pushing every idiot through Gymnasium and then university. First what you yourself have just experienced in S., then the same, even worse, during his university studies, and in the end we get a teacher or district judge or government official, completely uncultured but conceited, and holding forth to his cronies about his experiences as a student which he never confessed to his wife. It would be a hundred times better if someone like Meyer simply learned a good trade.''

"Someone like Meyer would have been bad at learning a trade, not good.''

"I am afraid that's true, Ulrich; at least the way we knew him he was fit, at best, for a bartender in a disreputable bar. But the mistake lies deeper down. If all her life Frau Meyer was conditioned to believe that only a man with a title is a real person, and if this Frau Meyer, who is a competent, self-supporting seamstress, starts shaking in her knees when she has to go to the town hall to talk about her taxes with a bespectacled accountant with a title, then something is wrong, and that has got to have an effect upon the way she brings up her son. She probably inoculates her offspring, who may even have some talent, with so many false ambitions and anxieties; so palpably beats into him respect for the real men, men with titles, believing herself to be doing something worthy of finding favor in God's eyes; she probably makes him take so many bows in the wrong places,[58] and calls upon God for help against the nastiness of her child in case he should dare make an independent move; consequently, the poor fellow is a wreck before starting his life. And is it a wonder if, in that case, Herr Archibald Meyer believes he has to behave according to the station of an incipient titleholder by going to bars, acquiring a girlfriend, a lady from the city revue if at all possible, and so forth and so on—and at last fails his examinations and makes his mother unhappy?"

Christoph had sat up while talking and really didn't look at all like an incipient titleholder.[59]

"And whose fault is this whole calamity?" he continued. "It's the fault of none other than the fashionable people, the so-called upper class that everyone envies and watches to learn how to live with success. And this upper class itself is largely composed of rotten, pushy people, with the souls of lackeys, who mix[60] flattery for superiors with brutality for inferiors, grand phrases for the outside with decay on the inside. And the few decent people and families who might count for something withdraw into themselves in disgust with this hollow, conceited society. Ulrich, that's where the whole problem lies. We need a genuine upper class again,[61] but how can we get it? You yourself say it's always up to the few big wheels, then the rest topples over. That simply means, doesn't it, that Ulrich Karstensen and Christoph Brake, not Archibald Meyer, must set the tone? We can't get around it, and false modesty is out of place in this matter."

Ulrich had sat up during these statements and was watching Christoph attentively. He enjoyed listening to Christoph developing his ideas with such assurance and passion, and although he was happy to be caught up by them and agreed with Christoph's line of thought, he still kept his own clear perspective and sometimes saw matters more simply but also more profoundly than Christoph.

"You are right, Christoph, it simply depends on us. But are we really completely immune to the poisons of[62] vanity and pushiness that infect people nowadays? Look, I often have to think of my mother in this context. She surely is a simple woman; and a village organist, as my father was, certainly isn't part of the upper class. Nevertheless, I have never found in my mother a trace of false ambition or anxieties while in contact with superiors. With all her modesty, she moves with total freedom and assurance wherever she goes without wanting to be something different from what she is. She knows precisely, of course, what it means for me to be in your house and I really don't think she is depressed about being unable to return the favor to your parents. And yet I can sense how she fears that, because of my contact with you, I might some day aspire to be more than I am by birth and by environment, and that someday I would have to be unhappy if I realized the unbridgeable gap between your origins and mine. What I mean to say is — Mother is as free of the modern disease of pushiness as one can be. And if I wonder where she gets that, then there is only one very clear answer: from her Christian piety; that is what makes her so assured and so modest simultaneously. And now I often think that everything has come to the state it is in today because most people no longer have what Mother has. Do you understand? And Christoph, if it is ever going to change, if someday, as you say, there is to be a new, genuine, and responsible upper class — don't you think that then such people must again have what Mother has? Or else they'll immediately revert to their previous state."

Ulrich never found putting his thoughts into words as easy as Christoph did and this difficulty always pained him somewhat.[63] But his warmth, his personal manner, and his great inner modesty always lent a quality to his speech that was winning and engaged one's attention. While Christoph enjoyed presenting the same idea in ever new variations of phrase and illustration and had at his disposal a great facility for expression, Ulrich always stated his thoughts just once, and then left it to Christoph to assimilate and integrate them into his own train of thought and give them a form in which they could become effective.[64] That was why Ulrich[65] was usually the listener and also gave the impression to others that, essentially, he was the echo of Christoph's views. In reality, those views were often Ulrich's thoughts, observations, and feelings, which he had stated briefly and often clumsily; Christoph presented them in brilliant form and with the most personal conviction. Ulrich felt profound joy and satisfaction in having found in Christoph such an appreciative and persuasive interpreter of his own thoughts.[66]

What Ulrich had just said had never been voiced yet between the two friends, not because Ulrich might have been ashamed of

these thoughts in some fashion—that simply didn't exist between
the two—but because Ulrich always took a long time letting ob-
scurely felt matters work themselves up to the clarity of consciousness and word. Christoph was surprised and sensed immediately
that something had been said that was quite decisive and new for
them both. This had happened to him several times before with
Ulrich, and what Christoph had just said about the necessity of
the new upper class had, itself, grown on the soil of some similarly
startling ideas of Ulrich's.

Christoph looked at Ulrich. "So you think we would have to
have more religion if we want to occupy a responsible position
someday?"

"I think, Christoph—rather, I wonder—no, I think we would
have to be Christians."

Christoph looked toward the lake, saw young Martin paddling
along on his raft in complete absorption. He looked toward the
forest, toward the wide sky.

"A damned old-fashioned thought!" he said.

Ulrich didn't answer.

"And just as uncomfortable."

Ulrich remained silent. A long silence reigned.

"You spoke about your mother, Ulrich," Christoph started in
again, "and you know how much I like her—excuse that dumb
expression! But I am thinking now of Papa and Mama. One probably can't call them Christians, at least not in the usual sense of
the word. They don't go to church. We say grace at table only
because of Little Brother. And yet they are just as little infected
as your mother by the spirit of false ambition, careerism, titles,
and medals. They prefer a good laborer or artisan a hundred times
over some conceited person with the title of 'Excellency.' Why is
that?"

Ulrich pondered. "That is because, without knowing, and at any
rate without saying so, in reality they still live in Christianity—an
unconscious Christianity."[67]

Christoph became restless; he got up and walked, barefoot, back
and forth in the thick grass.

"You are a funny character, Ulrich, the way you say that all of a sudden, so assuredly and calmly, as though it were quite certain."

Ulrich sat without moving, his arms around his drawn up knees.
Suddenly he laughed. "You needn't worry, Christoph. I didn't
kneel on the Salvation Army's repentance stool, and I didn't join
any sect."

Christoph, too, had to laugh at this idea. What would Ulrich
have had to confess? A grotesque idea! No, that's not what he had
meant. Christoph continued pacing, pondering, then he stopped
before Ulrich. "Something seems to be wrong, Ulrich," he said.
"As far as I[68] know Christ didn't differentiate between the good
and the bad, the just and the sinners, the decent and the mean.
In my opinion the so-called publicans were lousy traitors to their
people and the prostitutes belonged then, as now, together with the
Archibald Meyers. And from the confirmation classes with the odi-
ous Pastor Schönrock I remember Paul's words: 'There is neither
Jew nor Greek, there is neither slave nor free, there is neither male
nor female.'[69] So according to the Christian doctrine all people are
supposed to be equal and [illegible]; 'God hath chosen the weak
and base things of the world,'[70] or even, 'The weaker and poorer,
the better.' That's the exact opposite, after all, of what both of us
experience and think and want every day. How then should Christianity of all things be able to help form a new upper class, an elite?
That would only lead to hopeless equalization."

Ulrich was silent again. He had to think of old Frau Karoline
Brake.

"And your grandmother, Christoph? I am sure she is serious
about Christianity and probably knows more about it than most
ministers. Do you think she doesn't differentiate between people?
Doesn't she think, just as we do, that there must be a top and a
bottom and that everything depends on the right people being
on top?"

Christoph hesitated. "I don't understand it. Somewhere there
must be a contradiction," he said.

"Yes, I don't understand it either, Christoph, but that's what
you are here for, to get it clear. Unfortunately, you are the more
intelligent of the two of us, after all."

"Don't talk bosh, Ulrich."

At this moment splashing was heard from the lake, and a little later Klara's red bathing cap could be seen. She had just woken from her nap and was now taking a second dip. A few seconds later a cheerful cry came from Martin who, with a leap, dived off the raft into the pond and surfaced next to Klara. That was the signal for Christoph and Ulrich to leave their problems behind. They raced each other down the hill and soon were in the water.

"Oooh, cold!" gasped the two who had come out of the hot sun. Then they saw the hermit-like figure of Franz throw aside his raincape and book at the water's edge and swim towards them. Now the pleasures and games of the morning began again.

Suddenly a sharp, jarring voice cut through the gay laughter in the lake. On the shore stood a young, slim man in yellow hunting boots and a brand-new green uniform, a riding whip in his hand.[71] "Get out of the water, you riff-raff. Can't you tramps wash off your filth somewhere else? Get out of the lake; come on, come on! Hurry up! Pronto, pronto![72] Do you think I have time to waste, you damn louts?"

So it went, on and on, in that impertinent voice which—lacking any sensitivity—wanted to turn even a peaceful lake in the forest into a military drill yard. Martin, closest to the shore, was the first to come out of the water and stopped in apprehension.

"Will you come here, you lout!" Yellow Boots addressed him rudely.

Martin had pulled himself together meanwhile, and approached, looking defiant.

"What, you want to be fresh too? You just wait, you whippersnapper. We'll drive that out of you, you'll pay dearly for your pleasure." And with these words, the man in uniform grabbed Martin by his ears and pulled him close.

At that same moment Franz had come ashore and no sooner had he seen the hunter touch his young brother than he jumped at him with such a leap that the man in uniform stepped back a pace in alarm.

"Let go of my brother this instant," shouted Franz, "or—"

The hunter let go of Martin,[73] pale before the threatening, angry expression Franz had assumed.

"I advise you not to touch me," he stammered and raised his whip. "How did you miserable[74] pack of townies and tramps get here anyway? Here, put on your rags and scram and be glad I don't whip you on the seat of your trunks."

Beside himself with fury, Franz yelled, "And if we were miserable townies and if our clothes were rags, who do you think you are, you costumed ape, you great brute? A petty, miserable cartoon character, that's what you are.[75] Remember that!"

The man in uniform turned red in the face. "And you have stolen to boot, you thieves," he screamed, and kicked the pot with the leftover mushrooms so that it rolled into the water.

Now Christoph and Ulrich had arrived too, with Klara behind them, and the three tall young men with their strong, bare bodies were standing around the hunter, who was only a few years older than they, and vainly dressed. Christoph had caught the word "thieves" and stepped up close to the enemy with icy calm.

"You will now, loudly and clearly, take back everything you have just said," he said with frightening determination. "We are neither tramps nor thieves. Now you know. So!"

The hunter began to feel uneasy, but tried once more. He raised his whip and shouted, "You green boy! You can't intimidate me!"

At the same moment Ulrich grabbed for the whip and held onto it firmly.

Christoph said, "I forbid you to call me 'du' and once more demand that you take back your words."

"I wouldn't think of it!"

"Then you will tell me your name and state at whose orders you are here."

Klara intervened. "Let it go, Christoph. Can't you see, the man doesn't know how to behave and has gone too far. It doesn't pay to argue with him."

"No Klara, this affair will be cleared up. I won't let something like this pass."

The hunter, meanwhile, must have noticed from the young people's demeanor and manner of speech that he had taken the wrong approach to them and probably wanted to back out of the situation somehow. He tried an artificial smile, but met with the stern countenances of the three young men. Klara looked at him[76] mockingly; Martin was already close to laughter. Ulrich still held on to the whip.

"Take your words back," said Christoph once more with an almost terrifying severity.

At this moment the hunter visibly paled. His glance was directed past his young opponents toward the wooded trail on which he saw people coming.

"Let me go," he suddenly said in a totally different, almost imploring voice, "the matter shall end here.[77] You misunderstood me, gentlemen." And he tried to get his whip and leave.

"We wouldn't think of letting you go. The matter is in no way ended, and we didn't misunderstand you at all," Christoph replied most calmly.

"What is going on here?" he suddenly heard a man's deep voice ask behind him. "Kruse, what is the matter here?"

The brothers and sister turned in surprise and saw an elderly gentleman and, behind him, a family coming out of the woods.

"Just a joke, Major,[78] a small joke," the man in uniform stammered with an embarrassed smile.

"A very bad joke at any rate," said Christoph.

"No joke at all, but an enormous audacity," Franz burst out, still in a great rage.

Ulrich was still holding on to the whip.

"Let's have quiet first," cried the major. "Well, Kruse, talk!"

"Major," Kruse stood at attention, "I wanted—I thought it might bother the master and mistress if people went swimming here on Sunday. So I requested the gentlemen to remove themselves, and a little exchange of words arose; not worth mentioning, Major, really not worth mentioning. Terribly sorry, Major."

Meanwhile the major's wife had approached with her three children: a young man of about twenty, a daughter about fifteen, and a twelve-year-old boy. Kruse bowed low and in embarrassment.

Now Christoph stepped in front of the major, bowed briefly, then said in a clear, firm voice, "We apologize deeply for this incident, Major. My name is Christoph Brake and these are my brothers

and sister. We went swimming here, not realizing that the lake is
private property, but we don't let anybody call us tramps, louts,
and thieves. We also don't think being threatened with a riding
whip is a joke. I ask you, Major, to call this gentleman to account,
and we will then, naturally, leave immediately at your request.
We once more apologize for our mistake."

These candid words and the upright attitude of the seventeen-
year-old who stood in front of the major without embarrassment,
though with his hair still wet and clad only in his bathing suit, compared favorably with the false smile of the young man in the full-
dress uniform. Christoph was just about to take his leave after
another brief bow when his glance met that of the girl, who now
stood next to the major and looked at him calmly from big dark
eyes. For a moment he was thunderstruck.

"Please stay," he heard the major say, and then continue with
noticeable asperity, "Kruse, you know perfectly well that I do not
want such behavior here, indeed I detest it. If you learned it in
the barracks, it's bad enough. I never tolerated or needed it there,
either. I consider it disgraceful. Who gives you the right to call
a person you don't know a lout, tramp, or thief just because he
happens to be in your power? Such an insult reflects on the person
who utters it. Kruse, you will now apologize to these young people
and take back your words!"

"Major," stammered the young man in the full-dress uniform,
"Major, I beg you most respectfully not to ask that of me. It's impossible; it's against my honor."

"Against your honor?" thundered the major. "What kind of
honor is that which is too proud to admit to a wrong and set it
straight? A prank, an idiocy, a stupidity for which I don't give
a fig. Kruse, where did you learn that? Who turned your head and
heart with these notions? Come to your senses, Kruse, and do what
you have to do as a man of honor."

With a last convulsive motion Kruse pulled himself together
and cried harshly, "Major, I most respectfully beg to be dismissed
from your services. I cannot give up my concept of honor."

"Go, go, Kruse," cried the major, "I won't keep you. But[79]
beware of making yourself and others unhappy!"

Kruse, who had become deathly pale, clicked his heels and saluted. The major returned the salute and Kruse left.

Shaking his head, the major looked after him and stood for a moment deep in thought. Then he turned to the young people and said, "So it is up to me to apologize. Please believe me, I regret this incident deeply—more deeply than you can comprehend now. I feel sincerely ashamed, for," he said bitterly, "I detest such behavior. Much evil, much unhappiness will come from it in our country."

A noticeable appearance of gloom passed over the gray-haired man's features during these last words.

"We are very sorry," Klara said in alarm. "We didn't mean it to happen that way."

"A blessing that we are rid of him!" cried the major's wife now. "That fool doesn't belong in our woods. I am so happy that I don't have to see him anymore—and Harald, be honest, you are too." She continued gaily, turning to the young people, "We owe that to our young, unknown guests. Now let's recover from the shock and sit down together for a while."

"Madame," said Klara now,[80] "you are very kind to ease this uncomfortable situation for us. But we were about to leave, in any case, and really don't wish to disturb you any longer. Also, we promised to be home for supper to spend the evening with our parents. I thank you very much, but I think we had better leave now."

"No, my dear child," said the major's wife, gazing at Klara with pleasure, "you mustn't flee from us so quickly. We are curious now to find out who the people are who invited themselves to our place today, and to whom I owe gratitude for the unexpected pleasure of no longer having to see the foolish face of our forester's assistant. Besides, the next train back to town doesn't leave until six o'clock, and if you walk by way of our estate you'll be at the station in half an hour. I assume you want to go to the town?"

"Yes, Madame."

"Well then, come and sit down with me for a while, and first let's properly say hello to each other." The major's wife put her hand out to Klara.

"My name is Klara Brake and these are my brothers Franz, Christoph, Martin, and Ulrich—or rather, Ulrich is Christoph's friend, but he is like a brother to us," Klara said.

"Did I hear you correctly?" the major interrupted her, "Is your name Brake and are you connected in some way with Professor Brake in town?"

"That's our father."

"Is it possible?" the major cried, as if he were a new person. "Then you are the children of my old friend from school, Hans Brake? And I saw you all ten years ago on my last visit to your parents—but you won't remember, of course. What a strange meeting and how nice![81] But didn't your father ever talk about me? Sophie,[82] children, you know about Hans Brake, don't you? Yes, Hans Brake and Harald Bremer were as well-known forty years ago as Castor and Pollux or David and Jonathan."

"So you are Major von Bremer!" the young people cried at once. "Of course we know who you are! We know very well but we didn't know, Major, that this was where you lived."

"You scarcely could know, but I'll explain that to you later. Before anything else, however, let's do the introductions. I'll address you with 'du,' of course, and for you I am Uncle Harald, this is Aunt Sophie, and—come children, say hello to one another— this is Johannes, our second oldest who is named after your father; that is Renate; that is Georg."

When, during the general cheerful handshaking, they got to Ulrich, the major said, looking with friendliness into Ulrich's clear face and good, calm eyes, "And this Ulrich, whom you call a brother, naturally belongs to our union too."

Ulrich looked at him frankly and gratefully and shook hands with him.

Upon this surprising turn, Aunt Sophie proposed a short walk around the lake, then a return to the castle, to take afternoon tea in its park. There they could talk and get to know each other at leisure. Everyone agreed and, after the Brake children had dressed, the group started out. In front between Franz and Ulrich was the major, followed by Christoph, Renate, and Johannes, then Martin and Georg. In the rear walked the major's wife who had linked arms with Klara, and soon the conversation started up among them all. Klara was asked to talk about her parents, her grandmother, and her brothers. Georg explained the origin of the raft while Martin reported his discoveries at the shore. Christoph[83] listened to Johannes[84] describe life on a country estate, and was particularly interested in everything about the relationship between the owners and the day laborers. Renate said nothing.

The major walked in silence for a while between his two young companions and, from time to time, glanced with particular curiosity at Franz, from whom he had hardly heard a word spoken up to this point. He sensed that the young man had not yet recovered from the incident with the forester's assistant. Without preamble the major said, "One must be able to forget, Franz, or else one wears oneself out."

Franz glanced up in surprise and then said candidly, "Yes, I find that very hard!"

"Franz, such a stupid fool can't possibly offend you!" The major spoke with peculiar warmth and insistence.

"It isn't the offense, Uncle Harald, it's something else."

"What is it then, Franz?"

"I don't know how to express it without making it sound trite— it's the general aspect of the matter."

Something gloomy passed across the major's features. Word and answer were separated by pauses. "Hmm, what do you mean by that, Franz?"

"I mean—that something like that can exist at all, and I wonder what causes it. It has a destructive quality that is much worse than a personal insult. It's hard for me to express, Uncle Harald."

"I understand, Franz."

"If we didn't happen to be our father's children—if we really were some poor kids from the town who wanted to go outdoors on a Sunday—and then such a scoundrel, excuse me, came along who wanted to vent all of his stupid self-conceit and brutality on us, then we would simply have to take it." Suddenly he burst out passionately,[85] his rage driving tears to his eyes, "I simply can't bear it, Uncle Harald, that someone takes advantage of another's defenselessness in order to trample on him—and then that disgusting, ingratiating smile. The swine would have hit Martin if I hadn't jumped between the two of them." Franz was shaking with agitation. The major put his arm around the young man's shoulders.

"Franz, Franz, I know exactly what you feel—much better than you suspect," he said gravely. "But believe me, my boy, that's not the way to handle it; I know. One must be stronger than these tormentors of men that you find everywhere nowadays, in schools, in offices, in the military. One must engage in battle against them, in pitiless, ruthless battle—but for that one must be stronger than they are, or else—" The major broke off suddenly.

Franz, surprised and touched, saw a great sadness in the eyes of the experienced old man. His glance met Ulrich's, who seemed equally touched.

"Sorry, Uncle Harald, that I started in again on that stupid affair."

"I brought it up again too, Franz; it's stuck in my gullet also."

Franz was seized by a powerful, warm trust in the major. How did it come about that such an old officer, of all people, seemed to understand him, even sympathize with him? He was, moreover, impressed by the major's calm kindness beneath which such strong passion still simmered. There was an aura about this unique man that was like the sun when it breaks through after a passing thunderstorm, though now and again thunder and lightning will still be heard and seen in the distance.

Franz got up his courage and asked, "Uncle Harald, do you really believe what you said before, that 'one can get along without this kind of behavior in the barracks'?"

"Have you been in the army already, Franz?"

"No, it'll be my turn in the autumn. But I have heard a lot from my friends."

"Then you already know what to expect."

"Yes."

"Good."

The major again fell into his puzzling silence. "I want to tell you something, Franz. Perhaps you'll be able to use it some time. In the matter we were talking about it isn't just a question of style, but of much more. You mustn't be oversensitive; when people are learning a rough trade such as a soldier's it doesn't happen without a rough word, without an occasional curse, or even without a dirty joke. That's often very hard for someone who isn't used to it. But he'll have to fight it through and learn that there are also different people and ways of life. Perhaps he'll even succeed in prevailing against the majority—all the better if he does. But it isn't necessary, and no one should wear himself out over that; it's not worth it. A man must know that there is a lot of filth and brutality in life. He must come to terms with it and still remain himself. We understand each other up to this point, Franz, don't we?"

"Yes, Uncle Harald, absolutely. For the last two years I have been helping[86] a former minister who resigned his pastorate to work full-time in the poor quarters of our town.[87] I took over a youth club there and have to visit my boys' parents in their homes. There I heard and saw more than I can say;[88] I know that people become involved with brutality and filth without it being their own fault, and these people particularly are most kind and willing to help without saying a word about it."

"Good," said the major tersely. "Incidentally, I doubt that such kind of work makes much sense, but let's leave that for now. So, anybody who gets upset about every coarse word is an old maid, and we don't want to have anything to do with that sort of thing. But—it is something quite different if a man uses the power he has over others to humiliate, debase, defile, and destroy them.[89] That is no longer a question of style, that is blasphemy. Not merely against the people but against the office he holds, also. It is a desecration of all genuine authority and the destruction of all human community. It is the dead-certain road to anarchy. Franz, I don't know where it comes from, but there is in all of us a dark, pernicious instinct to misuse the power given to us and thereby to destroy life—our own and that of others. We must hate and passionately oppose this really evil instinct wherever we meet it, first of all in ourselves; for don't think, Franz, that it isn't inside you too, only waiting for a chance to have its fling. It is something uncanny that there must be power, yes, that power is something holy, which comes from God and yet that it so easily makes us into devils, turning us into great or small tormentors of men. Look

86

at the little forester's assistant: a charming, harmless, good-natured comrade among his own kind, and perhaps a good, loyal, ordinary head of a family someday. But he is a devil when his ridiculous bit of power tickles him, and a miserable sycophant[90] at the feet of his superiors. There are many vices, but none brings greater unhappiness to man than the misuse of power, especially such misuse at the hands of petty people. Again and again history has produced great tyrants; they, in turn, called forth great counter-forces whose judgment they rarely escaped. They are demi-gods who aren't subject to ordinary human judgments. They rise and fall in a few years; but the petty tyrants never die out. They live in the favor of their various masters and bask in it, thereby escaping earthly justice. It is the petty tyrants who destroy a nation at its core; they are like tubercular bacteria which secretly destroy a flourishing young life.[91] They are not only more dangerous but also stronger, tougher, harder to get hold of than the big ones. They slip through your fingers when you want to grab them, for they are smooth and cowardly. They are like a contagious disease. When such a tyrant sucks the vital strength from his victim he simultaneously infects him with his spirit; and as soon as this tyrant's victim gets hold of the least bit of power himself, he takes revenge for what has happened to him. But this revenge—this is the horror—is not directed against the guilty, but against innocent, defenseless victims. And so it goes, endlessly, until at last all is infected and poisoned and dissolution can no longer be stopped."

The major stopped, drawing breath. "Nevertheless, boys," he continued, "one mustn't be discouraged by the seeming hopelessness of the struggle. Whoever succeeds in toppling one of these petty devils may boast of having saved many human lives; he becomes a benefactor of mankind, even if no one else is aware of it. Many right-minded people of our class have acquired the habit of smiling about these petty tyrants and of regarding as fools those who have declared total war on them. But smiling about them is as foolish and as irresponsible as smiling about the tiny size of bacteria or about the doctor who saves a few lives during an epidemic and then falls victim to the disease himself. To be sure there must also be strategists and soldiers in this war, as in the battle against an epidemic there must be those who use a microscope to research the cause of the disease, and others, like doctors who attack the individual case. But woe to him who mocks the sacrifices made during this war!''

Expressions of an almost solemn gravity lay on the faces of the two young people. They felt as if they were about to be sworn in. And they sensed that the man addressing them had been compelled to make his own great personal sacrifice for this cause, even if they knew nothing of it. But how could they ask him if he himself didn't say? The respect they felt for this unusual man, walking again in silence between them, didn't permit any probing into his personal fate.[92]

He began again himself. "You make me happy. When we get home I want to give you something to read.[93] Remind me. But now let's talk of something else."[94]

Ulrich now had to tell about his growing up in the village as the organist's son, about his father's death and his mother's move to the town so that he could go to the Gymnasium, and about his life in the Brake's house.

Without noticing, the three men, in the course of their conversation, had hurried far ahead of the others and now stopped on a small spit of land where there was a bench. Looking out to the lake that lay, a calm oasis in the sun, each gave himself up to his own thoughts about their conversation.

Soon Christoph and Renate were heard as they approached, their voices carrying in lively conversation. When they had started out, Christoph found himself walking next to the young girl. He looked around for a moment to see whether a third might join them, but the other groups had already formed naturally and the two were left together.[95] Christoph felt an unknown shyness rise in him. He wanted to invite Renate to walk with him simply with a friendly glance, but then his eye was caught by hers and could hardly look away. For the first time he experienced the eye's peculiar law, its power, its warmth, and its danger. Soul, body, and blood crowd together in the eye, and there is no longer any strength left for the word.

"Come, Renate," he heard himself say, as if with a stranger's voice. He had dropped his eyes, but they had absorbed an image that they wouldn't give up: the dark blonde, curly hair, the white skin, the large, deep-brown eyes, the slender figure in the light shantung dress. On the narrow path they were walking close to each other and Christoph was aware of Renate's dress touching him from time to time.

"Your land is beautiful," he said finally.

"Yes, very beautiful. But so confining," Renate answered.

"Confining?" Christoph asked, astonished. "How big is your estate?"

"Oh, it's about two thousand acres, but there isn't any distant view and there are too many people here for me. I am still home-sick for South Africa.[96] One year is not enough time to adjust."

"But here you are in your homeland."[97]

"That's just the point, Christoph. That simply isn't as clear to me as it is to you. My mother is an Englishwoman; I spent the first fifteen years of my life in South Africa, a British country, and was happy there. At home we speak German, I have a German name, and I love my father more than anything[98] — and my dear oldest brother lies buried in Germany. I walk through the woods with my father almost daily and day by day I come to love our estate more. But sometimes it seems to me as if I were choking. It is then I'd like to ride on horseback through the endless plantations and see the few Negro huts, but otherwise no people, no people at all. I think it's the people here who make me feel so confined. There are too many and they are so different."

"And you say that, Renate, although you have scarcely a few hundred in your village!" Christoph cried. "Don't you like people at all? Do you think it's terrible that you met us today?"[99]

"I'll tell you frankly, I was really apprehensive when we first met you and thought you'd spoil our Sunday. But then I soon found out how different you are from most people.[100] You can't imagine how I hated that forester, so much so that I was sometimes ashamed, and I was happy when you defeated him. No, it isn't true that I don't like people at all. But I always like just individuals. And then—you mustn't be angry when I tell you[101]—and you really won't be able to understand—" Renate hesitated. "I really wouldn't want to hurt you."

"Please, speak out, Renate!"

"All right, if you want. Do you know what a black mammy is? We had one as almost all whites did. She was in my home since my birth, nursed and cared for me, she sang those first little songs to me and told me stories from the bush. She was always around me, she was always good and kind, she was completely bound up with our house, she loved all of us and served us loyally, quietly, and with boundless devotion. When she heard we were going to move to Germany, her heart nearly broke. With tears in her eyes she begged my parents to take her along. My mother was willing, but my father refused. We didn't understand at the time, but he was right. Mammy would have simply died here. But I can't forget her, and if I now imagine her on quiet evenings at the farm sitting in front of the hut together with other Negroes and singing together— they sing so beautifully, with such warm voices—and the way they used to smile at us and say hello with such friendliness when we were riding on horseback across the plantation in the evenings— yes, then I get a terrible longing and I feel as if I have left my soul there and can't find it again here."

There was a silence while Christoph vainly searched for words. Renate continued,[102] "It really is that way, Christoph. Here I sometimes don't know if people actually have souls. When I think of our self-important, vain, grumpy inspector or the village mayor or that forester, for example, I feel nothing but a sense of formality, compulsion, and officialdom. I feel as if I should practically freeze to death near them. Yes, everything is so gloomy, cold, hard, and difficult here that the soul has to hide in some corner where it can barely breathe and live."

Renate spoke with such simplicity and genuine feeling that everything he could have argued seemed empty and flat to Christoph. It so rarely happened that he failed in conversations. He loved discussions and was considered an awesome opponent among his peers. But this young girl rattled him. She said impossible things and yet—what could one reply?

"But your Negroes are slaves, so to speak," he said—and immediately noticed he had said something stupid.

Renate laughed frankly, "Slaves? Nonsense! At any rate they are people with souls, and everywhere here I see made-up characters who think themselves terribly important. I'd really like to know where the slaves are, there or here."

Christoph gave a start.

"Forgive me, Christoph, I have just spoken with a little bitterness. I didn't want to do that, and I know I mustn't become bitter under any circumstances, because it's Father's homeland, your homeland, and possibly my own homeland too some day. But believe me, it's hard to understand and to love this country and these people here. One needs a long time. Most of all one probably has to meet people through whom one can understand the life, the fate of this country."

For the very reason that these last words were spoken without design they aroused strong emotions in Christoph.[103] It seemed to him as if someone were looking for his help,[104] and Christoph was one of those people who hunger for tasks. Where in school he saw a comrade needing his protection, his aid, or even his counsel and guidance, where he could take on some responsibility for another person, there he was in his element, and no one dared get in his way while he was taking care of another person. If anyone did, he fought like a lion and was a terrible enemy. Christoph had a strong and healthy confidence in himself that he was able to help other people and bear responsibility for them. Without such tasks his life seemed empty to him. It didn't matter to him whether or not he liked his protégé; he acted less out of love for the individual than from a need for responsibility which was essential to his nature. As a result, some of his comrades thought him proud and overbearing, but others had boundless confidence in him so that more than one came to confess his life's story to Christoph and ask for his help. At first this had frightened Christoph. He had always instinctively resisted pondering the inner processes in the lives of his comrades,[105] so he had at first refused to hear confessions of a personal sort when they were presented to him, saying to the person concerned, "You'll have to cope by yourself with your inner difficulties. I don't want to know about them." But the other answered with a sad smile, "It's easy for you to talk," and it was just this attitude of restraint that increased trust in Christoph even more. Later—it was a year ago, perhaps—Christoph had asked Ulrich for advice.

"There must be a point to it," he had said at the time, "that the inner life of another is by nature inaccessible to us, and that no one can see into our inner being. We must obviously be meant to keep it for ourselves and not share it with another."

After reflecting for a long time Ulrich had answered, "Except with God—or with a human being given to us by God, who can keep as silent as God does."

Christoph hadn't replied and had fallen into deep thought. Nothing more had been said between them at the time, but the relationship of the friends to each other had been set on completely new ground by Ulrich's words. Christoph knew only then what he had in Ulrich. Once he knew that, he was able to bear with greater patience the trust brought to him by other comrades, even though he sometimes suffered from the burden of it.

He still liked best facing a definite task,[106] and such a task appeared now after Renate's last words. Renate needed to learn to understand and love Germany. For that she would need him. He couldn't think of it without his heart beginning to beat. This young girl, who was stepping out beside him so freely and assuredly, who had seen so much more of the world than he had, needed him. He was to be allowed to do something for her. Without meaning to, she had asked for his help. And it was such an immensely exalted and important task. Christoph was to become Germany's interpreter for the girl looking for a homeland here. Germany? What did Christoph himself know of it?

He and Ulrich had taken a few long trips in recent years and hiked through the Black Forest, East Prussia, and especially the Weser country with great joy. They had gone swimming in countless wooded lakes in the district of Mark Brandenburg, had seen the sun set between the pines on their shores, and set up their tents for the night. The two had been more deeply moved by the old brick domes and gates of small northern German towns[107] than by the high art of southern German churches and monasteries. They had gone out on the North Sea with fishermen in the middle of the night and had seen the stars rise over the sea and the shore and the hardworking men. Yes, all of that was Germany—but how could one express that in words? Christoph and Ulrich had needed only brief, casual cues to communicate on these trips. Apart from that there had remained impressions which neither could put into words. That you had to see with your own eyes, experience it and take it in with all your senses. Renate would have to travel,[108] to see Germany in order to love it.

But what would these trips have been for Christoph without Ulrich? Ulrich with his warm enthusiasm and great perceptiveness had belonged to that landscape and those towns; the country had opened itself to the friends only through the medium of the living soul of the other. So wasn't Germany really the people, not the things? Wasn't Ulrich, wasn't his parents' home—wasn't this what Christoph meant and knew as Germany? The musical evenings, the garden parties, the grandmothers, and the pictures of the grand-fathers—all these images passed before Christoph.

But then there was also that forester's assistant, there were the dissolute seniors from the Gymnasium, there were the many self-important, grumpy characters Renate had mentioned—and they were Germany too; they were Germany on its way down: the en-dangered, brittle Germany; Germany in need of a good, strong hand to get well. Renate should first get to know the good, healthy Germany. Of course, she had her father, but he could only be the single great exception for her. Now she had to find out that[109] there was a Germany from which this father, this exception, had come; a Germany to which he owes everything and to which he will always belong. Renate had to come to the Brakes' home, she had to see the parents and the brothers and sister, she had to come on hikes with them, and Ulrich had to be along, and Klara too.

Would Renate and Klara get along? They seemed immensely different. Klara knew nothing and wanted to know nothing but the home of the parents and the brothers and sister. A natural intelligence kept her from bothering with problems whose intel-lectual insolubility was clear to her in advance and which on the other hand had already been solved for her by life itself. She went her way and with total calm and assurance tackled the tasks given to her. She would hardly understand Renate's questions and problems, and yet the manner in which she lived would answer them simply and honestly. Perhaps that was exactly what Renate needed. Yes, Klara had to help.[110]

So ran Christoph's thoughts. He couldn't think without planning. But could one actually plan anything here? Wouldn't the intention, the plan, have just the opposite effect with a girl like Renate? Christoph felt all his ideas and plans dissolve, even in the making. He had never before had that experience.

Suddenly he said, surprised at himself, "I think that all of that will come by itself, Renate." These words were like a liberation for both of them.

What came by itself first was that the two got into a really free and easy conversation.[111] They didn't question each other; what each wanted to say of one's life, one's views, one's closest friends, was to be said freely.[112] In this way one of those rare and happy conversations came about in which each word is taken as the free gift of the one to the other. As it goes with gift giving, first there are only small, groping signs, timid unspoken questions as it were, as to whether the other is ready to receive a gift—unwanted gifts humiliate giver and recipient—but the acceptance of one's gift is the greatest gift the giver receives. Precisely because everything depends on the inner freedom of the giver and the recipient no one who is aware of that fact gives or takes everything all at once. It is a slow, free process of mutual bonding.

It is no different with such conversations as Christoph and Renate now began. There are conversations in which the partners challenge each other; other conversations are like violent explorations; still others are noncommital chats that barely veil the distance, the strangeness, and the indifference between people. But when a conversation is mutually giving and receiving there is neither violence nor indifference. The unspoken remnant is a hint of undiscovered treasures of still concealed wealth in the other which will reveal itself at a given hour. While Christoph and Renate were very different in their ways of life, their views, and their desires, there was still a natural accord in their essential attitude toward the other. When after walking for a half hour they reached Renate's father and Franz and Ulrich, they had learned much from each other, but above all they knew that they had exchanged gifts, and they radiated youthful happiness to the group which had become preoccupied with serious thoughts.

With kindness the father pulled his daughter to him, brushed her hair from her forehead and said, "My dear child—well, isn't it beautiful here after all?"

"Very beautiful, dear father," answered Renate, Christoph beside her.

"On your mark, get set, go!" they heard Martin's voice command, and the two boys came racing along the last stretch.

"Another dip in the water till the others come," Martin begged, and soon both had thrown off their clothes and were cooling their hot bodies in the shining lake.[113]

Frau von Bremer and Klara had taken their time. Some way off one could see the two tall women approaching slowly along the shore, conversing comfortably,[114] the older woman a slender and still youthful figure with her full, blonde hair, and the young one in a light-colored linen dress she had embroidered herself over which hung low her thick, heavy braids. In spite of all external differences the same free, composed, confident walk of the two women expressed an inner relationship, a certain shared spirit. Only women from old families walked that way, women who—like their mothers before them—have always known themselves safe under the protection of their fathers, husbands, or brothers, and safe within the realm of their families. But these women will also walk like that when disaster strikes and forces them to stand alone; that protection under which they once lived surrounds them at every step, even in the hour of greatest desolation, like an invisible power that no one dares touch. Women of this demeanor and carriage are kin whatever their origins.[115]

Klara was talking about the life of her family, about Grandmother, Little Brother, and her own homely tasks[116] which she had taken on when she finished school in the spring. Her day began punctually at five-thirty in the morning; she took care of her own room, at seven breakfast had to be ready for her parents. On the table every morning during the summer there was a bouquet of fresh flowers and, depending on the season, a dish filled with either strawberries, currants, raspberries, or radishes and another plate with chopped herbs, as Father liked them. Klara didn't mention that she always read a chapter from the Bible before beginning to work.[117] At seven-thirty she had breakfast with her brothers, then she sat at the head of the table, substituting for her mother, who enjoyed accompanying Father on his way to the clinic for a short distance. For years the daily breakfast of the brothers and sister had consisted of cocoa and dry rolls; on Sundays there was butter. A little later the brothers left the house and Klara took Grandmother's breakfast to her small living room on an old-fashioned silver service.

When Klara knocked on the door the grandmother took off her glasses and put a marker into the old Bible which she had been reading. Klara entered, kissed her grandmother's hand and received a kiss on her forehead. She put the Bible in its place next to the writing table, offered Grandmother her arm and led her to the small, enclosed balcony with a view of the garden where she had breakfast throughout the year.

Then came the all too short half-hour without which Klara couldn't imagine the rest of the day. She sat with her grandmother, no needlework in her hand for once. She saw to it that Grandmother had everything she needed; now she was able to talk with her, completely relaxed.[118] Usually they talked about everyday things and events, about the little changes that each day brings with it even in the most organized household. They also talked about the brothers and friends, but only rarely if ever about the parents or older people. Without the grandmother ever voicing general precepts and rules of conduct—or perhaps precisely because she didn't do that—Klara learned to love her daily chores through these simple talks.[119] She learned that details must not be taken too seriously but should not be underestimated either.[120] Her relationship to the arrangements and the members of the household took on an inner order and symmetry that pleased her. She heard Grandmother speak candidly about other people, without arrogance or asperity and without in any way damaging the mutual bonds between them. More than she consciously realized, she received[121] the blessing which a kind heart such as her grandmother's bestowed on a home.

While Klara was inclined through her simple, straightforward nature to reject, indeed to condemn easily, anything different or strange, she became thoughtful when her grandmother talked about changes in human conditions, customs, and modes of life which she had seen during her long life. The grandmother's mild, tolerant, and often surprisingly open-minded way of judging human nature contrasted sharply with her bluntness and inexorability if one started to talk about Christianity and the church—which didn't happen very often.

"There is nothing funny here," she said, "and only those who are tough here and stick completely to the truth may be gentle in life and occasionally even smile about the foolishness of people."

Klara hadn't quite understood this so far but she felt nevertheless that this apparent contrast had fused into a unity in her grandmother.

"I can't imagine Grandmother not existing someday," Klara said and then continued the report about her day, about several hours of piano practice, about the free afternoon hours, and about the last task of the day—playing from the *Well Tempered Clavichord* for her father when he came home late. "All of us especially love Bach," she added. "There isn't a Good Friday when we don't listen to his *St. Matthew Passion* together, and hardly a year goes by without our hearing the *Mass in B Minor*. For the last few months, we have been studying the *Art of Fugue* under Ulrich's guidance. I can't see why people find this music so hard to understand; for me it's the clearest and the most accessible music there is. But Mother isn't quite of our opinion either. She loves Brahms and Richard Strauss better and sings their songs very beautifully."[122]

"Do you want to be a musician someday, Klara?" asked Frau von Bremer.

"No, I never thought of that. Also, I don't have enough of what it takes, and I don't want to do something halfway. I'll stay at home and some day I'd like to get married and have a family."

The simplicity and warmth with which Klara said this made it clear that she wasn't speaking of her personal happiness but of her vocation.

Frau von Bremer took a strong liking to this young girl who was going her way so calmly and assuredly, untorn by inner dissatisfaction, and much too proud to pursue shortlived pleasures. She wasn't one of the daughters of our time of whom Frau von Bremer had met so many abroad: those girls who wasted their days with cocktail parties, tea dances, and adulation of film stars. She also wasn't one of those emancipated half-men. But she also was no future old maid who with her virtue and excellence would walk through the world a living reproach to all others. She was a born mother who had experienced the joy of a good family life from childhood and now carried it within her as a possession she could never lose.

Could Klara be the companion and sister for Renate that Frau von Bremer had been seeking for such a long time and had yet to find? Would Klara be able to help Renate overcome her homesickness for South Africa and feel at home here? It was difficult enough for the mother that she herself had become more distant from her daughter since they had settled in Germany. What Renate sought from her English mother, a means of preserving the memory of South Africa and her longing for its plantations, she couldn't give her—much as she would have liked to—without wronging both her husband and her daughter. But she couldn't give her the sense of feeling at home in Germany, particularly as it had to mean something quite different to Renate from what it meant to her. For Renate Germany was the whole future; for her it was most important not to go through her whole life with an unhealed wound. Renate was young enough to start afresh—to forget—or at least to remember without pain. It was different for the mother. For her Germany was her husband and her children. But her roots were, and remained, English. She had learned German for her husband's sake when she was young, and because she detested a fractured and badly spoken language, with such unusual mastery that no one noticed any longer that she was a foreigner. For many years she hadn't spoken a word of English when she was alone with the children. Their school and their world in general saw to it that they grew up bilingual. But above all, the parents had fought against any tendency in the children toward a slovenly mixing of the languages, which happens so easily with people living amid two languages and destroys genuine appreciation of a language's uniqueness. Harald von Bremer was immensely grateful to his wife for her sacrifice, and when the two sat alone together in the evenings it usually happened, probably as an unconscious expression of this gratitude, that Harald spoke English with his wife, and his English was as good as her German. Since they had been in Germany and the children were old enough, they often spoke English when they were all together, but they were very careful not to do so in the presence of others, including the servants: they would have considered that tactless.

While the sons changed languages without really noticing, for Renate the hour during which the family was alone and spoke English was dangerous. The memories became overpowering and the return to German often aroused in her a serious inner resistance, even defiance.[123] Sometimes they couldn't do anything with her for days and she couldn't come to terms with herself, and suffered from that. Whenever the mother tried to talk with her then she had to recognize that she wasn't equal to it. Good words, sensible reasons, kind persuasion, and serious admonition couldn't accomplish much at all. So the mother had to leave the daughter alone with her great problem. Renate's relationship to her mother alternated between stormy love, in the hope of again finding the lost homeland in her, and profound disappointment when she saw that the mother wouldn't allow her to wallow in the past. Frau von Bremer looked around for help. Of course Renate was attached to her father with all her heart, but then for her her father had been the South African farmer and plantation owner for fifteen years; now, when she took her morning walks with him through the forest she could never rid herself of that memory. Her love for her father was for him and didn't transfer to the Fatherland. The brothers didn't understand Renate; they called her behavior moodiness and it often angered them.

"One can control one's feelings and needn't have everybody else suffering from them," the taciturn Johannes once said. But that was unfair to Renate because she herself considered any exhibition of inner personal processes to be reprehensible and exercised the utmost self-control. But homesickness[124] had become a real illness for her with high fevers that couldn't remain hidden from others, much as Renate tried to hide them.

"How would it be, Klara," Frau von Bremer was saying now, "wouldn't you like to stay in the country with us for a few weeks?"[125]

Frau von Bremer concealed the real reason for her question. She knew that friendships desired and planned by parents were always rejected by psychologically independent children such as Klara and Renate and never came about. It could hardly be otherwise for in that case a child sees in the friend his parents intend for him nothing but a model for the virtues he lacks in the eyes of his parents, and thus the "friend" becomes their pedagogical device. It is as if they are saying: "Look, Fritz isn't like that"; "Hans wouldn't ever do anything like that"; "Greta[126] gets up much earlier, is much neater," and so forth and so on. By way of countless such remarks the intended friend turns into a bugaboo, a scarecrow, in no time flat even though he may not deserve it. Forced friendships are no good, Frau von Bremer knew. Either Klara and Renate would find each other on their own or not at all.

Klara was surprised; half apprehensive and half happy. She hadn't spent a single day of her life away from her parents or brothers. The invitation seemed too sudden.

"Thank you, Aunt Sophie," she said, "but I don't know what to say. I think I am needed at home, and besides I have made all trips and done everything together with my brothers up to now and wouldn't[127] really like to be separated from them. Forgive me for being so frank."

Frau von Bremer was wise enough not to be the least bit offended by this unmistakable refusal. Better this way than to have accepted right away, she thought. Klara knows what she has at home and she doesn't know us at all. A girl like Klara doesn't run toward uncertainties just because they are something new, an interruption of everyday routine. She prefers what is certain, lasting, proven. She doesn't wish for experiences, for changes, for the unknown, which make the lives of so many young girls unhappy nowadays. Why should she? She has everything she needs, she has a full life. "We must live more intensely,"[128] a worldly-wise young lady had told Frau von Bremer the other day, and had made very clear just what she meant by that. Probably Klara would just have shaken her head with a smile in astonishment over that. She did [not] need anything like that; she lived more intensely than these extravagant people. "It's all right," Frau von Bremer told herself. "She is hard to win over, but when she is won she holds fast. In any case I could have told right away by looking at her that Klara is one of those people who would rather extend an invitation than accept one. Even though with adults that is often a sign of superiority, unfriendly coldness, or of being tired of people"—and Frau von Bremer had to reproach herself a little on this account—"with children it is the most infallible sign of a happy family life."

"Then I'll make another suggestion, Klara," Frau von Bremer said kindly. "You and your brothers together can stay with us for a few days, but before that we'll all come to town and visit your parents."

It was soon settled that Frau von Bremer would get in touch with the Brakes the very next day, which she would have to spend in town with her husband because of some errands, and if it was all right with the parents—she could check today by telephone—she would bring the children; then they could get better acquainted.[129]

"Do you agree, Johannes?" the mother now asked her grown-up son, who had been walking by her side without saying a word, quietly listening to the conversation with Klara. Frau von Bremer was used to her son's taciturn manner and would have been surprised had he interposed in the talk.

Klara had not felt oppressed by his silence either, because she sensed that no rejection, indifference, or superiority lay behind it, but simply a quiet, introverted personality. Although Johannes had sunk into an even deeper silence since his oldest brother's sudden death, his parents didn't worry, and his brother and sister loved their brother almost more tenderly than before; this was because a feeling of peace, reconciliation, clarity, and acceptance had radiated from Johannes since that difficult experience, and that made all of them feel better in the days and months of mourning and inner suffering.

"Of course, mother," answered Johannes. And what these three words conveyed wasn't weak compliance, but clear agreement.

The big news of the plan for tomorrow was at once submitted to the rest of the family and happily approved by all. Talking animatedly, the group soon reached the big meadow nearby which belonged to the castle; it was surrounded by old trees, and at the end could be seen the long, low structure of the castle with its mighty terrace lying in the afternoon sun. Soon a long table was set in the shade. There were towering mountains of sliced country bread and plain yeast cake. Dishes with butter and fresh honey and stout pitchers with milk were brought. Two mighty bowls filled with gleaming strawberries made a great show on the festive white tablecloths. The mistress of the castle invited all to sit down. She poured some cream into the cups in front of her, asked everyone separately how many lumps of sugar each wished, and then filled the cups with dark golden-brown tea. At this the youthful guests, ignorant of this English custom, exchanged astonished glances; the tea at home was weak, and the children were only allowed to drink it with a lot of milk. Here they became acquainted for the first time with that strong, aromatic liquid, whose taste and attraction they had never really discovered at home.[130]

Before the conversation began once more, the major spoke. Unfortunately there wasn't enough time today, he said,[131] to show his dear guests the house and tell them something of its interesting history; they would all have learned, meanwhile, that he had been living here with his family for only a year after living continuously in South Africa for fifteen years. That he hadn't visited his old friend, the father of his young guests, during this year was because of his and his family's wish to live in seclusion after the death of their oldest son two years before (the eyes of Franz and Ulrich met involuntarily). They had wanted to end this isolation and quiet and now a kind fate had, totally by surprise, guided to him the children of the best friend of his youth. He took that as an especially happy omen, and would now do his part in getting the two families to meet and become more intimately acquainted; perhaps the fathers' friendship might be renewed among the children. Time would have to tell if this would happen. But because it was his former friendship with the father of his young guests which had brought them together here, he thought they might like it if he were to use the short hour remaining today to tell how his friendship with Hans Brake had come about, for he supposed that their father had not told them this story yet, and for good reason.

The major's friendly calm manner of speaking aroused in the Brake children a great desire to hear him tell the story. They knew little of their father's youth in any case because he never talked about himself.[132] So they begged the major to give them this great pleasure. There was general silence and the major began.

"I was thirteen when my parents, who were still living in this castle at the time, sent me to Gymnasium in town and boarded me out with an old aunt. Until then I had lived at home as an only child and had had private lessons. I was the undisputed leader among the children in the village and no doubt my parents thought it a danger that I had no contact with boys my own age who were intellectually and physically my equals. It was almost taken for granted that every playmate had to obey and submit to me. I don't think I ever abused my relationship to weaker persons, but also it never occurred to me that I might meet my master someday. I was very happy about my parents' decision to send me to the Gymnasium;[133] I was looking forward to the new companions, and already dreamed about the games I would show them and the war games in which I would lead them. I was so naive and inexperienced in my self-confidence[134] it never occurred to me that someone might dispute, or even unreasonably begrudge, my position.

"So one day I went to school for the first time, full of confidence and pride. The turmoil on the stairs and in the building, although I had never seen anything like it, didn't worry me in the least, but pleased me exceptionally well. The director, to whom my father had handed me over, himself led me to my new class. 'You are lucky,' he said looking at me closely. 'You are joining a very special class; we have never had one like it. I hope you'll enjoy becoming part of it.' He opened the door. I saw a group of about twenty-five students crowding around a boy standing in their midst animatedly speaking to them. Their heads turned to the door and they stayed where they were when the director entered with me.

'Well Hans, what is going on today?' the director asked the boy in the middle. The other boys stepped aside and made way for him. Only now could I see him clearly and I'll never forget that first impression: a slender but strong-looking boy with an imposing head, thick, dark-brown hair which could not be parted, intelligent brown eyes, and a somewhat protuberant nose, stood in front of us simply dressed in a light-colored shirt and belted trousers, straight and self-confident.

'We had to settle a class affair, sir,' he said politely.

'Some foolishness again?' the director asked.

'Yes, but everything is straightened out again,' Hans answered firmly.

'Fine, Mayor,' the director said (in an admiring but rather childish tone of voice). Hans frowned.

'Why do you sulk at that, Hans?'

'Because I don't like hearing that name, sir. My father is a mayor, but I am not.'

'All right Hans, I am bringing you the new student.'

"At the director's words, all eyes turned toward me. I was looking at Hans.

'His name is Harald von Bremer, you'll look after him for the first few days and introduce him to the life of your class. Well— good luck, Harald!' and the director was gone.

"Hans looked at me calmly, like one used to such tasks. He came toward me, shook hands, and said, 'For the time being your seat will be here on the[135] front bench, Harald; that's the way it always is here until we get to know a new student.'

'Where are you sitting?' I asked ingenuously, and noticed many astonished eyes looking at me because of my question.

'I am sitting all the way in the back,' Hans answered.

'Then I want to sit next to you,' I said.

"There were giggles.

'Quiet!' commanded Hans, and the giggles stopped. Then he

turned to me; our glances met and held. 'That isn't possible, Harald,' he said, 'perhaps later on.' He seemed surprised somehow.

'And why isn't it possible if I would like it?' I asked, more uncomprehending than challenging.

'Because Hans gives the orders here and not you!' cried a high, shrill, child's voice belonging to a short, ambitious-looking boy who was hoping for a gratified look from Hans.

'Shut your dumb mouth, Meyer!' Hans erupted, and the small boy drooped; then he said to me very calmly, 'Well, not because I give orders here, but because the class wants it that way—that's why it has to be. You must understand that, Harald.'[136]

"Our glances met again, locked for a moment. For the first time we silently matched our strength against one another.

'So here is your seat,' Hans said, and led me to a bench that I shared with a good-natured looking older boy. In a voice which was already changing—half adult, half still child—he said to me as I was sitting down beside him, 'Don't be angry. Hans is[137] a great fellow; if only these damned copycats and ambitious pushers weren't here; they're going to spoil him yet.'

"The schoolbell rang, the teacher entered, and class began."

"If you go on telling your story in such detail, Harald," Frau von Bremer interrupted, "the children won't be able to do anything else."

"That's all right, Sophie," the major answered. "It's the story of their father; nobody but I can tell it to them, and I want to do it thoroughly. Eat and drink, children, and listen; your father really was a great fellow."

"It became obvious, even on this first day of school," the major said, continuing his narration, "that there were no problems for Hans in any subject. He was undoubtedly the best in the class. His Latin conversation with the professor was practically a pleasure and Homer, whom we had just begun to read, seemed to present him with no greater difficulties in the original than in the translation by Voss.[138] I kept completely quiet on this whole day and wasn't called on either, but had time to observe in peace. I noticed that the other students' comments were unusually bad in all questions requiring independent thought and judgment. But Hans and his whole attitude attracted my attention all the more. His superiority to his fellow students seemed to be such a foregone conclusion to him that he didn't show the smallest trace of ambition or vanity. He was who he was, and as such he was the undisputed and absolute leader, but equally the idolized favorite of his class mates. He had hardly appeared in the schoolyard during recess when he was surrounded by a crowd of boys, big and small. Then he would organize games or entertain himself however he pleased at the moment, and even the older students smiled kindly at him when they met, occasionally staying nearby to listen to his conversations and even taking part in the games he arranged.[139] In short, they tried in every way to show their special liking for him. I never saw anything like it in my later life. Hans simply was the school's idol. And I must repeat, the astonishing thing was that Hans accepted it all without the smallest trace of complacency or pompousness, but as the most natural thing in the world. He laughed, romped around, got excited like any other boy,[140] but when he commanded, all obeyed automatically, and none would have dared to use any sort of vulgar language in his presence.

"During the first recess I walked through the schoolyard by myself;[141] everything was very different from the way I had imagined it. This Hans had upset my calculations. Leaning against a tree, I tried to watch him. Suddenly, someone tapped me on the shoulder. It was the student with whom I shared the bench.[142]

'I am supposed to look after you, Harald,' he said.

'Who told you to?' I asked.

'Hans. Did you know that little Meyer has started his dumb talk again? He said you are really arrogant because you are an aristocrat, and so forth, or else you would also be with Hans like the others. But Hans shut him up with something forceful and said that you could be where you wanted, it wasn't any of Meyer's business, and he could understand quite well that you wanted to be by yourself. And then he said "Paul, look after Harald for a while." Incidentally, I would have come anyway. I don't take part in everything like the others.'

"Greatly astounded, I looked into the friendly, calm face of my older comrade, astounded at his commission as much as at his last words. I began to feel trust in him.

'And why don't you take part in everything?' I asked, hoping to hear something important.

'I don't really know,' answered Paul in his slow way, 'at any rate, it's a long story. We'd better talk about it some other day. But I'll tell you one thing: it has nothing to do with Hans; he is a great fellow.'

"The thoughts shot through my head: What is it that has nothing to do with Hans? And with whom does it have to do? For the second time he had called Hans a great fellow. Obviously everyone agreed on that. I hadn't yet framed these thoughts into a question when Paul went on.

'It probably won't be easy for you here, at least that's how I see it. With me, it's different; I am average, not so noticeable. But they'll pay a lot of attention to you. You'll have to see how you make out. At any rate, you can depend on me.'

"My head was humming. I understood almost nothing that Paul had said and looked at him questioningly. 'Just wait,' he said. 'You'll understand; there isn't any rush after all.'[143]

"The bell was ringing for the last class. What had this quiet, somewhat awkward boy been prophesying for me? I only awoke from my dreaming when the bell signaled the end of the hour and the school day.

"In front of the school Hans asked me: 'Shall we walk home together?'

'Fine,' I answered, 'I am going left across the bridge.'

'I have to go right through the park,' said Hans.

'Too bad,' I said, 'then it won't work.' I noticed Hans looking at me with surprise.

'Yes, too bad,' he only said, and I saw how the whole group of students crowded around him in order to walk him home. Had he expected the same from me? I wondered. The idea hadn't occurred to me at all. I had started to walk home when Paul caught up with me. It turned out that he lived only a few houses away from me.

'You should have gone with the others today,' said Paul.

'But I don't live in that neighborhood.'

'The others don't either.'

'That's their business,' I replied, 'I am going my own way, at any rate.'

"Paul said nothing. We walked beside each other in silence.

'They are going to spoil Hans yet,' Paul suddenly mumbled to himself, 'if something doesn't explode soon. All this idolization is bound to turn his head. They are just aping him. It's a wonder he is still sane and doesn't care about all that stuff. It's not good for the class either, by the way. Nobody can thrive or advance. And a lot of the fellows who flatter him are really disgusting. Hans is much too childlike; he doesn't notice at all.'

"Paul was maybe two years older than Hans and I. I had noticed already that he was a poor student; he learned slowly and with difficulty but, as was apparent now, he possessed independent judgment and his own life style which others accepted. As he was quite without personal ambition and very good-natured, he was the only one in the class, next to Hans, with some kind of special position. We said goodbye.

"During the following night I tossed and turned in my bed for a long time, and was hardly able to fall asleep. I saw Hans before me all the time. Then I had a dream. We were in the schoolyard; the other boys were playing games. I stood alone leaning against a tree and watched them indifferently. Suddenly a ball flew past my head as if intentionally, so that I started, and I saw little Meyer smile; soft little giggles swelled to a roar of laughter deafening me like a hurricane. At the same time little Meyer visibly grew bigger and bigger. He held a pen in his hand that gradually grew to gigantic proportions along with him until suddenly, laughing derisively, he splashed my face with it so that ink ran down my cheeks. I raged with fury, wanting to get at him, when I felt my hands being tied to the tree from behind by several boys. At this moment Meyer's face changed to an expression of pale horror, his body shrank to the size of a dwarf's. Hans had appeared and stood in front of him. He wore full, splendid robes and a beret of velvet, as I had seen on pictures of mayors and other high government officials. Meyer had become so tiny by now that he was jumping around among the shoes. Hans kicked him and he was dead; I exulted and was ashamed in the same moment. Meanwhile all the other students had thrown themselves on the ground. Only Paul stood a little apart with his arms crossed; he kept shaking his head. Countless times he repeated,[144] 'It isn't good, it isn't good.' Hans smiled at him. Then he ordered the others to get up.

"At that moment all eyes were directed at me and everyone cried shrilly as with one voice, 'The new one didn't abase himself!' I got terribly upset, for all of them came at me in a sudden metamorphosis. In the shape of all kinds of flying vermin—bumblebees, mosquitoes, horseflies—they stung, bit, and tormented me dreadfully. I lashed out on all sides and, left and right, masses of vermin fell to the ground dead. Then I saw Hans before me with his astonished look. With one leap I was on him, grabbed him, tore his robes off him in pieces. A terrible wrestling began. Hans kept his astonished expression. We were gasping for breath and exerting our utmost strength. Neither could force the other down. The schoolbell rang, but we kept on wrestling, it rang louder and louder, unceasingly, deafeningly. Students and teachers stood around us in a big circle. I heard the director shout, 'Hans, Mayor, give it to him!' A deep, calm voice then said, 'Shut up!' and hit him on his mouth with a notebook. It was Paul.

"Our strength began to ebb. Chest to chest we felt each other's hot breath. I didn't believe I could hold out any longer. Then the dwarf Meyer who was meanwhile alive again, suddenly crawled toward me from behind and bit deeply into my leg. I felt a terrible pain, but Hans kicked Meyer so that he totally disappeared into the ground. That was the catastrophe because as he did it Hans lost his balance for a moment, stumbled, and fell underneath me. But instead of lying on top of him, I jumped up and released him. I felt deeply ashamed. 'Excuse me,' I stammered. All the teachers and students around us had disappeared; there was dead silence. We looked at each other for a long time in astonishment. 'Come,' said Hans, and as if nothing had happened we went to our classroom and sat down side by side on the last bench.[145]

"The whole next day I couldn't stop thinking of that dream.

Whenever Hans passed me our glances met, but we hardly spoke. Paul was my only companion. During the following week it soon became apparent that my work was hardly, if at all, inferior to that of Hans. But I received no recognition for it; on the contrary I thought I could feel a growing antipathy to me from the class. In sports too, both of us were far ahead. The automatic result of this was that in team sports Hans and I always led the two opposing teams. For the first time in years the team led by Hans lost about as often as it won. But that didn't help me either. Hans played games with the utmost propriety; he would be terribly upset if someone on his side made even the smallest attempt to cheat. Then he would call his own comrades the most derisive of names. When his side lost he would only look at me with big astonished eyes, but the others I could feel were thinking revenge. During the recesses I continued walking with Paul, while the whole class gathered around Hans. After school our ways parted as on the first day. But although all seemed to run smoothly and peacefully on the outside, on the inside all kinds of garbage was piling up.[146] I talked with Paul about it.

'I have always known that something would happen between you two,' he said. Asked why he thought so since I didn't really have anything against Hans after all—and what could Hans possibly have against me?—he answered (and it wasn't really an answer), 'Perhaps a thunderstorm like that will clear the air in the class. It wouldn't hurt.'

"During those weeks of the approaching thunderstorm a few disagreeable characters from the class joined me and tried to conspire against Hans. They said he was tyrannizing the whole class and wouldn't tolerate anyone beside him, he was arrogant, hated me, and was just waiting to humiliate me in some way; it was time someone confronted him with strength, and so forth and so on. Since I knew that these boys sought me out only because Hans had treated them sternly because of some meanness or impropriety or other I immediately turned my back on them, stating that they should say all of that to Hans personally, and that I didn't believe them anyway. I heard from Paul that others were slandering me the same way to Hans and that Hans rejected it just as decisively as I had. I liked him for that. During my hours of leisure at home I often wondered what the cause of this ever-growing tension might be. I could find no fault with Hans and he, I thought, could find none with me either. I found his views sensible, his behavior always decent and kind; yes, I somehow felt a kindred spirit in his whole nature. So it could only be the fault of the other students. They drove us against each other and stood between us. They viewed my mere presence and especially my achievements and successes as a disturbance and an insult to their idol.

"One day the first of the skillfully laid mines went off. Hans himself came to me in the morning and asked me to join his group during the main recess. The paleness of his face and his trembling lips betrayed a strong inner turmoil that disturbed me. I couldn't imagine what he might want of me. When I joined the group there was a hostile silence. Hans began in a soft, trembling voice: Three classmates had reported I had asserted after the last game that he, Hans, was winning occasional team games only by cheating; that I had stated that he had been the only one to write the last Latin test without errors merely because the teacher, being afraid of Hans's father, was always telling him the text in advance; in the third place, I was said to have threatened to set a trap for Hans in the coming big games that he would remember for a long time. What did I have to say to that? Hans looked at me with burning eyes, awaiting my answer. It seemed as though the ground was rocking under my feet and I may have been just as pale as Hans. I just asked, 'Who said that?' Hans, at that moment probably believing me capable of a terrible act of revenge, said that wasn't important. I had regained my control and only said calmly that I wouldn't say a word in my defense until I knew who had slandered me; I would promise to take revenge on him by nothing more than disregard. Hans seemed impressed by these words. Again one of his astonished glances struck me. The class seemed to be seized by a certain unrest. 'Don't tell' and 'None of his business,' a few were murmuring. When Hans didn't answer right away, I said loudly and angrily, 'Then I have no further business here and I[147] won't speak a word with any of those present until all of you apologize to me for this infamy.'

"While saying that I looked at Hans openly and sharply and turned to leave.

'Stay here, Harald,' Hans said now. 'I can see now that we have wronged you. It was mean slander. I apologize to you on behalf of the class. If you want names, I'll give them to you. I promise you that nothing like this will ever happen again. I'll guarantee that.'

'Keep those miserable names to yourselves,' I cried in leaving, then turned back once more and said, 'Only it's a pity, Hans, that you thought me capable of that at all. You should know your people better.'

"For the first time I saw on his face an expression of deep perplexity, sorrow, and shame, and I regretted my words as soon as I had said them. With special baseness the slanderers had invented the kind of aspersions which would particularly offend Hans's delicate sense of honor. Now they had defeated not me but Hans. That hurt me. Decisively I turned back once more, stepped up to Hans and offered him my hand. He took it in silence. Then, paying no attention to the others, I walked away.

"I don't want to burden you now with all the details of the following developments, all of which I remember as though they happened yesterday," said the major.

"My position in the class was assured and protected from then on because Hans had given his word. However, the thunderstorm had not yet struck, but instead got blacker and blacker. I heard from Paul that a whole group of boys aimed at nothing less than[148] getting me removed from the school somehow. Hans was changed after the unpleasant incident. He seemed to have lost some of his spontaneity. Often I heard him use harsh words against comrades and saw him watching some of them distrustfully. To me he was as friendly and as proper as ever. I sometimes even felt something like warmth and affection coming from him.[149]

"The day of the big school games had arrived. Preparations had been going on for a long time. Hans had a lot to do with it; I didn't participate, especially since I hadn't been invited. However, I tenaciously practiced the required exercises every day and firmly intended to win first prize.[150] For these games they used a point system allowing not only for the determination of best of class but also of best of school. The latter was to be the celebrated victor, and in the last two years Hans had been best in the school. Meanwhile we were fourteen-years-old and young juniors. When we lined up on the playing field that morning Hans briefly addressed the class, and using noticeably sharp words insisted upon the utmost fairness and camaraderie in the upcoming competitions and even uttered somewhat dark threats against anyone violating these rules. Hans was looking bad; something severe and distrustful showed in the gaze with which he surveyed his comrades; nervousness showed in his movements. When he finished he gave me a brief glance as he walked by as though wanting to ask whether he could do anything further for my protection.

"In the generally festive mood this scene was somewhat depressing. But as it turned out, Hans was right. The first incident occurred around noon. As expected, Hans's and my performances were about equal; I was even leading by a little. Hans didn't seem quite up to his normal level physically or psychologically and hadn't done very well in some of the events. A tense whispering was going through the class: Hans wasn't going to make it today. Angry glances were directed at me. Then during the soccer match it happened that Hans received such an unfortunate blow that he swayed and lost consciousness for a moment.

'That was Bremer,' they were suddenly saying. When Hans—still half groggy—heard the murmuring, he only shook his head vehemently, 'That was certainly not Harald; that was someone else.' I immediately requested a decision from the umpire, and fortunately it was clearly established that I hadn't been anywhere near Hans at the decisive moment. It was evident to me that it hadn't been chance, but that one of my enemies had in the meanest possible way tried to get me disqualified. But since I couldn't prove that, I kept silent. Hans recovered quickly, immediately came over to me and, with a sincerely troubled face, expressed his regret over this new base effort to cast suspicion on me. I felt sorry for him. With his comrades he was mute. In the afternoon he succeeded in catching up to me in the point score by exerting his utmost strength. Later he told me that he hadn't cared anymore about winning at all but that he thought my not winning that day would be better for my sake. So it came about that in the evening we had identical scores; there was only a single competition left.

"Meanwhile the word had gone around all the classes that the decision on which of the two of us would be best in the school was due in a few minutes. So the two hundred boys of the school assembled around us. I was openly fighting for my victory, Hans for his—for my sake.

'Brake and Bremer to the pole vault!' the umpire commanded.

"This was a competition in which I was especially good, but Hans less so. Classmates, among them Meyer, brought the various poles for us to select from. I saw a few boys exchanging quick and furtive glances. Hans seized the first pole handed him, made a running start and jumped.

'Three meters, fifty!' called the umpire.

"A dissatisfied murmuring arose. Hans usually jumped much better. I was already sure of victory, took the same pole from Hans's hand, and jumped. Again: 'Three meters, fifty!' Disappointment! We repeated the exercise and both made three meters, seventy. The suspense was growing.

'The poles are too heavy,' Meyer cried and with a pale face and, as I later realized, a shaking hand, he passed new light poles to Hans and me. I was just balancing mine in my hand with satisfaction when Hans[151] grabbed it from me with a sudden motion, threw Meyer and his comrades a terrible glance that I couldn't understand and immediately started to run. He planted the pole securely and drew himself up on it with wonderful ease. I could see him pass four meters when at the height of his vault the pole splintered; Hans plunged onto the lower part of the broken pole. He lay still and silent.

"At that moment I understood everything in a sudden flash of insight: Hans's talk, the blow during the soccer game, the comrades' whisperings, and Hans's terrible glance at Meyer prior to the last jump. I only remember being the first to kneel by Hans's side, ripping off my gym shirt and wrapping it around his bleeding thigh. Hans opened his eyes and looked at me, I think I may say, as a friend looks at his friend.[152] 'I gave my word. They betrayed me. I knew it; this is the end,' he said softly.

114

"A deep, calm voice behind me said, 'Perhaps it's a better beginning.' It was Paul.

'It was Meyer and his people. It's not your fault,' I cried, and with threatening glances looked around for my enemies.

"Hans dismissed it with a motion. 'Well, I should have noticed and prevented it; I was too weak against them. But I was all alone, I had no one to help me,' he added softly, 'no true friend.'

'You have now,' Paul's rough voice said again behind me. Hans put out his hand and I took it. We didn't notice any longer that the others were standing around us.

"In a trice the news flashed about among the students. Meyer and his friends were seized and stood, deathly pale, inside a circle of older students. Hans got up with my help and supported himself on my shoulder. The competition was quite forgotten. Then a loud voice rang out; the senior in charge of the games called for silence.

'The games are over. Today's winners were Hans Brake and Harald von Bremer. Cheers, cheers, cheers. Meyer and all others who are guilty will be suspended from competition for the next three years.'

"While two hundred voices were loudly rejoicing, Hans and I were lifted up on the shoulders of a few seniors, Hans with my bloodsoaked gym shirt around his leg, I by his side. I could see Paul who stood below me having trouble hiding the tears in his eyes, and I was hardly better off."

When the major ceased a profound silence reigned. Martin was biting his lips, Christoph and Ulrich were staring ahead into space. "Yes, that was your father," said the major, "and so we became friends. I think both of us learned from that day something for our lives," he added thoughtfully and fell silent.[153]

After a while Christoph asked, "What do you mean by that, Uncle Harald? You didn't really have anything against one another personally, and your views weren't different. You were similar even in your personalities. How did all that happen anyway? I don't quite understand it."

"You are right," the major answered. "We were very much

alike, and that was just the point. Each of us was living the dream that he was really alone in the world, and all others simply existed for his sake.[154] This dream blinded us to one another. Although we couldn't reproach each other for anything, although we had been raised by our parents with the same views and concepts of decency and honor, although we even basically felt a certain affection and respect for each other, we couldn't bear the other next to us. Each believed the other was in his way and had to submit to him. If you wanted to use big words you could say it was a pure power struggle. Neither of us was aware of it, naturally, but the way we were a clash was inevitable. When we awoke from our dream we had learned that no man exists for himself alone in the world, but that he lives with others and must get along with them, and that this is good for people. Certainly one has to give up some things. One must learn to yield without giving up one's character. Yes, character is really formed only through such mutual living with one another.''

The attentiveness with which especially the young men listened to these words of the major was a tacit request for him to develop this point in some detail.

"In your lives," said the major, turning to the young men, "you will meet people again and again—and perhaps you are still like that yourselves—who believe it shows character to immediately and forcefully suppress any resistance, any contradiction, any difference; yes, who are proud of finding resistance and enmity because that provides them an opportunity to prove their power. 'Many foes, much honor,' it is said,[155] and 'Any yielding shows lack of character,' and so forth. That sounds very impressive—but it's sophomoric. The only people who talk like that are those who have no good judgment in human relationships, no contact yet with reality, and no sense of existing values. Eternal sophomores! They rate their own strength simply by the ruins they leave behind them; they think it meritorious to smash as much fine china as possible and they childishly exult at the clatter of the fragments. They consider it a sign of a strong character never to yield an inch, never to make way for another, never to compromise.[156] As long as we are children we may give ourselves over to such dreams of world

116

dominion for our little egos,[157] we may in our naiveté even enjoy finding followers because others believe in our dreams. But what kind of followers are they! Weaklings, flatterers, and—at best— dreamers themselves! The sooner we learn that with such dreams we sin against life itself, the better. Whoever hasn't heard this by the time he grows up is a disaster for his fellowmen and ultimately even for himself. Crushing another person literally or figuratively just because he is different has[158] very little to do with character. Truly it takes much greater strength of character to understand and get on well with another without losing oneself in the process. Peaceably living together with one another without knorking each other's skulls in is the real task in life. How ignorant he is who only sees weakness and cowardly surrender in that. No, this is precisely the real battle, often fought for a long time, tenaciously and with immense effort, before one advances a single pace. And what is the point? Not to leave the other on the battlefield as a corpse, but to obtain his consent to my will, or better: to establish a common will or consensus between him and me, thus turning the enemy into a friend. That will never happen without sacrifices on both sides, especially without mutual recognition and respect. Here alone is the field where character is proved and formed. There is no destruction here, but building; no realm of dream and fantasy, but the world in which people truly live together. Here too strength and power is used, not for its own sake but to serve human understanding and the quest for a better common life. Forgive me, I am getting carried away, but I believe no young man can learn this early enough. We Germans tend so easily to miss our grasp on life, not from wickedness, but from dreaming, delight in words, ideas, and feelings.[159] We find it more difficult to get together than others do. We remain individuals who do bloody battle against each other over the slightest differences—or else we surrender totally, submitting completely to the will of a single individual. But both ways sin against life as it really is, and they must fail. Life demands our being together and we find that so very hard. That was what Hans and I learned when we were fourteen, and never forgot again.''

The major broke off and said, with a glance at the two younger

117

boys and the empty bread and cake plates, "You may get up, boys, you aren't interested in these matters." With a lively protest the two declared they were, on the contrary, most interested in everything that was said and anyway, it was wrong of the adults to think all the time that boys couldn't understand their conversations; surely they understood more than people knew, and how could they learn anything if they were only supposed to listen to their schoolmates discussing sports and homework? Georg and Martin had said this so persuasively and as of one mind, that the major smiled and was pleased.[160]

Now Franz joined the conversation. What the major had said made him think of his senior-year history teacher.[161] He had been the only teacher whom Franz had loved and respected; he was very intelligent, really cultured, a fine, quiet man in contrast to the rest of Franz's teachers (from whom, unfortunately, he had always heard only terribly empty talk). His whole being had expressed a great liking, a sympathetic kindness for each of his students. He had tried to be fair to anyone who was serious about something; if someone used imitative, acquired, empty talk he could become really furious.

"However, I was never able to agree with him," Franz said, and he now very much wanted to know whether the uncle meant to say essentially the same as that teacher. Some things had reminded him strongly, others not.

"I'll never forget how he presented the great historical movements to us—the French Revolution, the Reformation, the origins of Christianity. Those hours[162] still reconcile me to my years in school which otherwise were a waste of time. Whenever the professor had finished one of these topics, a few lessons followed during which we were to draw conclusions from the material. It was as if the history teacher had become a different person in these lessons; before he had lectured with fire and passion, now there was a certain melancholy about him. He said history showed that all these great movements and ideas had brought disaster in the end. The French Revolution had ended in terror and was the beginning of mob rule in Europe; the Reformation had ultimately rent the spiritual unity of the West and in the end made it defenseless against materialism; Christianity had torn up the inner life of nations and individuals and[163] hardly anyone found his way back to himself.[164]

"But to prevent catastrophe, finally there had always been a mediocre compromise between the world and the new ideas, and in these compromises the essential and original impulse was buried. One could never simply say that without being branded a heretic and a misanthrope by society. Yet probably all of that was basically right. At any rate, it was the result of the lessons of history and of life—and we should remember it—that one can only live with compromise. Once I answered that what he called the results of history one could equally call its symptoms of dissolution and fall, and why, in that case, should one sniff around in the smell of history's decay instead of sticking to its high points and seeing the results and the lessons of history in *them*."

"You are a pretty skillful dialectician," the major remarked with a smile, "but you are only playing around with concepts after all."

"That's just about what my teacher said," Franz went on, "he said he didn't insist on specific words, but that one should remain truthful and honest about reality and not deceive oneself, for it was also necessary to have a clear picture of the so-called high points. In retrospect they looked pretty good, but that was only due to the great deception of the historians who were too cowardly to confront the facts. Ninety-nine percent of those who had to live through such 'great' times found them to be a single chain of pain and misery. My teacher regarded it as fortunate that it was only every few hundred years that a generation was made unhappy by such a so-called great time. 'What right have we,' he would exclaim passionately, 'to consider history only from the viewpoint of the few successful people, forgetting the blood and tears of the millions? I tell you, Franz, such writing of history is barbarism, acceptable for Oriental despots two thousand years ago, but a moral scandal after two thousand years of Christianity. Such writing again and again produces barbarism because it systematically makes people savage and base.'

"I was very impressed and unable to reply. 'It is the moral of the so-called great times,' my teacher continued, 'that people, their life and happiness, count for nothing, that human blood must be shed in order to consecrate the altar of some idolatrous idea. Don't misunderstand me,' he cried almost solemnly, 'I am not speaking out against the great ideas and the great men of history. Both are semi-divine forms and beings which from time to time intervene in the history of earthly men according to a scheme incomprehensible to us; they are at once wonderful and terrible, brilliant and destructive. Childish is he who tries to interpret the great ideas of history as the result of hunger and the great men as products of the masses. He has no notion at all of their fearful, superhuman power. Criticizing them is presumptuous and foolish. No, I bow down before these incomprehensible powers who—according to the wisdom of Holy Scripture—are born of the forbidden intercourse between the sons of God and the daughters of men.[165] The giants known to the legends of our nations are alive and can be seen on our earth from time to time, but we are dwarfs before them. Yes, dwarfs! Remember that! And that's precisely why we shouldn't act as though we were giants. That's precisely why I don't want talk about the great times. They are the arenas of mythical, semi-divine figures, but for the rest of us they are dreadful; in truth even the giants perish in them. Jesus, Luther, Cromwell, Robespierre, Napoleon—none of them really cared about the happiness of men even when they spoke of it, and each of them cried at the close of his own life's work as Jesus did: "My God, my God, why hast thou forsaken me?"' "

The major had listened most attentively to Franz who was speaking with increasing ardor. Now he interrupted him with a brief sentence, spoken quietly to himself, "An intelligent man, your teacher, but the last point was wrong. He should have excepted Christ; then everything would look different."

Franz gave the major an astonished and somewhat uncomprehending look, but once more continued his narration, which was actually supposed to be merely a question: "When I couldn't help myself in any other way, I asked our teacher whether man was created to be happy. He looked at me with an indescribably friendly yet sad glance behind which was a little smile, and said almost like a child, that he really didn't know. He also said he didn't know whether there was anybody who did know, but he would talk about it again with me in twenty years, then we might each know more.

"Well, he died a short time later. Perhaps he knows more now."

During these last words there was an expression of maturity on Franz's features that was beyond his years. "So now I want to ask you, Uncle Harald, whether what you said about living with one another also means that one can only live with compromises. I would find that terrible," he added almost boyishly.

"You touched upon more questions than we can discuss at a coffee table, Franz," said the uncle. "I agree with your teacher on many counts, especially what he said about great times and about the writing of history. It's true, the history of successes has been recorded more or less completely and there probably isn't too much of any consequence to be added. But now it is time — and this is a much harder task — to write the history of failures and the history of the victims of success; that is, to use your teacher's words, not the history of the giants and demigods, but of men. I don't mean the history of the ever-restless and rebellious masses, of conglomerations and explosions — those too are superhuman though subterranean mythical forces in some mysterious way connected with the great, successful men of history. No, I mean the history of those men who, tossed about between these forces, try to lead their lives through work, family, sorrow, and happiness.

"I have told you about Hans and me. We had both regarded ourselves as demigods until we realized — or sensed at any rate — that we were human beings who must live directed to one another, with one another, and beside one another. To our good fortune we became friends. Demigods have no friends, only tools which they arbitrarily use or throw away. I distrust anyone who has no friends. Either he is a demigod or, much worse, imagines that he is one. For me the main question for people and nations is whether or not they have learned to live with other people and nations. To me that is more important than all their ideas, thoughts, and convictions, and surely your history teacher meant something similar. But I wouldn't say that the result of history and of life is compromise. Whoever puts it that way still has his mind set only on ideas and must therefore resign himself again and again to the fact that no idea prevails in all its purity in life; then he calls that a compromise and sees it as nothing but a sign of the imperfection and wickedness of the world. I only consider man and his task of living with other men and regard the successful completion of precisely this task as[166] the fulfillment of human life and history. What seemed a misfortune to your teacher is to my mind the only happy thing for people. They don't need to live with ideas, principles, creeds, and moral tenets, but they may live with each other, meeting each other and assigning each other individual and proper tasks in this encounter. Only this way of living is fruitful and human.

"You wouldn't believe what changes took place after those competitions. Not only in Hans and me, but also in the whole class. Every day for weeks I was at Hans's sickbed. There we got to know each other and a quite new view of the world. I would say that at that time we first became human beings through one another. A new life started in the class too. The spell which had been cast over the class by Hans's nature and which had been further strengthened by my arrival, was now broken. The talents and personalities of our comrades could develop. Before there was only a retinue, now a healthy, strong camaraderie could grow. Even Meyer, who was to be expelled from school, but who had been kept on probation because of Hans's intercession, tried to make contact again. He had to start all over again from the bottom. Later he was thrown out after all, for other unpleasant reasons. Hans remained the class president till graduation, but only as the *primus inter pares*, and he made no decision without having thoroughly discussed it with me. Now was that a compromise created between Hans and me? I wouldn't call it that because that would devalue it. The decisive thing was not[167] what we both lost, namely our claim to stand alone in the world as demigods, but rather what we gained, namely a human life in community with another human being.[168]

"Now I believe that the same thing is also valid for nations and, in the last analysis, for all historical movements. Let me put it differently from the way your history teacher did. Like nature, history also develops a surplus of strength to reach a modest but necessary goal. Look at the thousands of chestnuts promised by the blossoms on the trees around us; how many of them will reach their goal of growing into new chestnut trees? Hardly a single one. Nature is extravagant[169] to assure its preservation. It is similar with great historical movements, conflicts, revolutions, reformations, wars; their results seem to us small in proportion to the forces expended. History too is wasteful when it aims to preserve mankind; it musters the most immense forces to lead people to a single, necessary perception. Even if we see and lament the incomprehensibly disproportionate relationship between the apparently senseless, fruitless sacrifices and the modest result, we must never underestimate the significance of even the most modest results. It is like the one chestnut in a thousand which roots unnoticed in the ground and promises again to bear fruit.

"The comparison is weak, of course; history is different from nature. But neither knows the rule, 'all or nothing'; they work by the law of preservation, of continuation and fulfillment of life, even at the cost of great sacrifices and renunciations. If there is a result or a lesson of history, I would not call it compromise, but love of real life."

The major took a deep breath, leaning back in his cane chair, and looked across the group of pleasing youthful figures into the flowering chestnut trees.

"Harald, Harald," Frau von Bremer now interposed, "that is the wisdom of age; it's not for the young. They want to hear something else."

"Maybe, dear Sophie, maybe," the major answered calmly, "but what harm does it do? The old and the young must live and get along together also. Is there anything more wrongheaded and offensive than for an old person to say only what the young want to hear? He is contemptible not only to himself, but also to the young; he violates the order of life. Who, for example, is preventing Christoph," he added laughingly, "who, as I have seen for some time isn't satisfied with me, from telling me his opinion just as frankly as I have been telling mine? I would even like very much to hear it, and I think we have a few more minutes before we have to think of further plans for the day. So, courage, Christoph!"

Christoph hardly needed this encouragement to state his doubts about the uncle's views. Had he been less well brought up or had he lacked his own sense of good manners, he would have interrupted several times already. So now the pent-up contradictions exploded with all their might. Christoph fastened on the last words of the major's discourse, and with his unusual skill in the use of language and his ability to present thoughts clearly and simply, he candidly confronted the uncle, and one of those situations arose where Ulrich looked upon his friend with boundless admiration and a feeling of deep inferiority.

"With every word you said, Uncle Harald," Christoph began, "it seemed as though[170] the ground were being taken from under my feet, as though I were to walk upon the sea. You call love of real life, living together and getting along, the ultimate lessons of history[171] and life. But what happens if there are already forces at work which render impossible, intentionally, any living and getting along together? What if a struggle has already been proclaimed to us in which there is no communication, only victory or defeat? What if a power rises up against us — like a monster that has been sleeping — which seeks to annihilate all that has made life valuable and significant to us? Yes, what if we must recognize in this power only the destruction of all orders of life, the incarnation of evil? Then yes, then it is no longer a matter of getting along with one another at any price, then it is a matter of the substance of life, of ultimate convictions, values, and standards, and then it is surely a matter of the 'all or nothing' you so roundly condemn; then the one who shirks the decision becomes a traitor to himself, to his past, to his calling, and to his family. I think there is far too much indolent peace among men and that we have to scare them out of that complacency. People look around for those who dare to hand them firm standards and have the courage to live according to them and to fight for them. And we, we should be the ones to take the helm and assume the leadership in this conflict, for we know what we defend and what we want. And because most people are lazy and cowardly, there have to be masters and servants, yes, I would almost say — slaves."

"Christoph!" cried Franz with the utmost indignation, "what you are saying is again simply frightful. You are working yourself up with your own assertions."

Christoph answered vehemently, "Please let me finish, Franz; I know that you think differently.

"Yes, I hold that Aristotle is right in his doctrine that there are some people born slaves by nature, and I think Schiller is wrong with his revolutionary slogan that man is free 'though he be born in chains.' But for the small group of masters, for the free, the elite, the leaders, love of life and happiness cannot be the ultimate norm. An unhappy human being is better off than a happy pet. I have just read the story of Don Quixote and Sancho Panza."[172]

"Oh, no!" cried the major, half serious and half laughing, covering his face with his hands, "but go on, Christoph, go on!"

Christoph blushed but pulled himself together immediately and completed his comments.

"I was going to say that we must not put philosophical and moral weapons into the hands of the Sancho Panzas, of whom there are more than enough among us."

"Oh dear, oh dear," cried the major again, "now I am undone. Don Quixote has thrown me off my horse. I am one of the Sancho Panzas, I am an *epicuri de grege porcus*, an arch-Philistine, and narrow-minded. Oh Christoph, Christoph, what have you done to me? Don't be angry, I beg you! You are right, my dear boy, in many ways. But," and the major shook his head and got quite serious, "what a strange generation you all are! The things that got us excited when we were your age, freedom and[173] brotherhood among men, you clever boys throw away as mere childish illusion.[174] Events cast their shadows ahead; animals grow thicker fur and the beaver a thicker layer of fat before a severe winter. What kind of times and tasks may lie ahead for a generation that even in youth has to think so severely in order to survive? It makes one shudder. But Christoph, dear Christoph, if you must be stern—don't glorify that sternness! If you must be inexorable to prevail—don't forget to be flexible, to relent wherever possible! If you must disdain life to gain it then don't forget to love it when you have gained it. But above all, beware of speaking lightly about happiness[175] and flirting with unhappiness! That is contrary to nature, contrary to life, contrary to man as he is created and as he barely manages to live—a poor sinner demanding happiness as a small sign of God's kindness. It isn't as easy to be unhappy as you might think, and whoever is truly unhappy doesn't disdain or inveigh against a happy man. I beg you, Christoph, don't make a habit of this[176] wild and wanton talk of the unhappy man and the happy pet. Why do you want to be masters, why do you want to lead, why are you willing to endure unhappiness if not in order to make others happy?[177] Unhappiness comes by itself, or better, from God; we needn't pursue it! Becoming unhappy is destiny, but wanting to be unhappy—that is sacrilege and a serious illness of the soul. Man has gorged himself on happiness; now for a change he[178] hankers after unhappiness, just from curiosity. I can't imagine anything more jaded, anything if you will—although I dislike seeing the word misused—more bourgeois than flirting with unhappiness.[179] It is a dangerous product of boredom and profound ingratitude.[180] Christoph, you are right in many things you said about our time and our tasks—but now one must also be strong and honest enough not to make a virtue of necessity, otherwise you turn the world upside down, and it won't tolerate that."

The major sank back into his chair and it seemed as though some image, some painful memory had seized him. "You said something very dangerous, Christoph," he said softly, "perhaps it is needed for Germany, but—you are playing with fire. Anyone who misunderstands you might do unspeakable damage."

What the major was thinking of while he said this, only his family could know, and the young guests sensed that the meaning and import of what he had touched on was something which only his family, not they, could understand.

While he was speaking, Christoph had not noticed the change that came over Renate. Now his eyes sought her, and he was deeply shaken when she lowered her eyes before him as if before a strange, frightening creature, and sat pale and huddled, seemingly frozen in the summer heat.[181] He had, he recognized at once, opened up a deep chasm between her and himself. Renate had[182] expected help from him and he had pushed her even deeper into her helplessness. He had given of his best, of himself, in what he had said. That was the way he saw Germany and the task of his generation. But Renate had heard in it the voice of the young Germany that made her suffer, that repulsed her and seemed to prevent her from ever feeling at home here. Had she understood him correctly? Did

126

his words about the born masters and the born slaves by any chance have some sort of inner connection with the appearance of the young forester whom, after all, Christoph abominated no less than Renate? Did Renate confuse this horrible caricature of all rule with rule itself? Could Christoph's meaning be so easily misunderstood? Indeed, were such caricatures perhaps the inevitable consequences when little people applied great ideas to themselves? And why had not only Renate but also the major become so noticeably serious? Whatever it was, Christoph felt that he had not been able to fulfill Renate's request, and it caused him pain. He did not manage to find Renate's eyes again.

Frau von Bremer, who could not permit her young guests to be depressed or discomfited by a reaction that had to be incomprehensible and puzzling to them, now proposed in a warm, motherly voice that they leave the table and continue the conversation some other time; now they should plan for tomorrow and the following days and then walk to the railroad station together. If today weren't Sunday[183] they would order the coach and horses. But unfortunately that wasn't possible. As she spoke, in a kind gesture she put her arm around Renate who was sitting next to her. The major, awaking as if from a dream, said he would be delighted if the young men would come with him to his room for a moment. Georg and Martin were already on their way to the stables where the animals were resting from the week's labor.

While Frau von Bremer drew the two girls to her and walked towards the park with them, and the major went upstairs with the four young people, the bells of the ancient church in the neighboring village began to ring in the evening.[184]

"Beautiful, isn't it, children," Frau von Bremer said, drawing a deep breath, "I longed for that in Africa sometimes. Listen how the old Misericordia lingers over its dark, unfathomable, low, warm tones; the clear, sterner voice in the middle is Justitia; and the lovely bright one above the two is called Pax.[185] When I first came to this estate, twenty-five years ago, the old minister told me the story of these bells.

"A Herr von Bremer, one of the major's ancestors, had the first

127

bell cast and presented it to the church during the Reformation; he gave it the name 'Misericordia'—mercy—so it would daily preach the gospel of God's mercy to the poor, frightened world. For about thirty years there was only this one bell. But when it turned out that the people, confident of God's mercy, misunderstood and misused these tidings of mercy by getting careless and sinning worse than before, Misericordia's donor left his son a request in his will to have a second bell cast with a sterner sound, and to call it 'Justitia' —righteousness; he was also to instruct the minister to preach the Ten Commandments more often, especially during the week, and to speak of God's mercy and grace only on Sundays. The son, devout like his father, fulfilled his father's last request, and for his part ordered that from then on Justitia alone should ring on weekdays, and Misericordia only on Sundays. The church chronicle says that there was an improvement in the congregation for a while. But it didn't last. Then God's judgment came over the congregation with the Thirty Years' War. Several plunderings and plagues left the village poor and depopulated. A great longing for peace with God and among men arose. So after the Peace of Westphalia was signed, one of the ancestors had Pax cast with its unearthly, gentle voice. The church chronicle tells that when the bell rang for the first time, the entire congregation cried loudly from joy and excitement.''

Frau von Bremer fell silent and the first gust of evening wind carried the full sound of the three bells into the park. The rays of the sun slanted on the mighty trees, some of which[186] might not be far behind the bells in age.

"People here call this Sunday evening pealing of the bells the 'great evening blessing'," Frau Bremer went on, "in contrast to the 'little evening blessing' on weekdays when only Justitia is rung. Mercy, righteousness, peace—that is a great blessing for a land indeed. Come, let's go to the pine hill for a while!"

"Yes, mother," answered Renate.

In silence they went through the park to a lane lined with tall pines that soon led to a peaceful meadow in the woods which belonged to the estate. Two deer, calmly grazing in the evening sun, took a long look at the approaching people and slowly walked through the tall grass into the woods. The shadows of the pine trees already lay over the larger part of the meadow; only the right side still had sunlight. Since the meadow was large and sloped down a bit, there was a hillock[187] just a few paces from the entrance to the lane where one could watch the sun setting over distant forests at a later hour. This little knoll, on which there were thick old pines, a few birch trees, and some heather, was called the pine hill in the family. In the center of the knoll, where one could see the entire length of the meadow, there was a wooden cross. A little beyond, on both sides, there were two benches of rough birchwood. There was no sign of a grave, but between the benches, and everywhere around,[188] wildflowers were blooming. The cross bore the legend: "Harald von Bremer" and underneath: "The souls of the righteous are in the hands of God, and there no torment shall touch them."[189]

"Here lies our oldest son, whom we lost a little more than a year ago," Frau von Bremer quietly said to Klara, pulling her down next to her on the bench. Renate sat down opposite them.

"It was his wish to rest in such a spot."

Klara said nothing, but looked at the cross and over the valley. The sound of the "great evening blessing" still came from the distance.

At the same time the major was in his study which, apart from some hunting paraphernalia and a few old pictures, was full of books, lining the walls up to the ceiling. The major was leaning over an old chest with metal fittings. Since getting up from the table he hadn't spoken a word. The young people stood by the open windows, listening to the same bells as did the women outside. Explained or not, the bells made their names and their tidings known by themselves, so to speak. Misericordia, Justitia, Pax— anyone who was at all receptive to the language of the bells could understand. The major straightened up now, with a small hand-printed volume in his hand. He walked over to Franz, Christoph, and Ulrich. Johannes remained a little apart.

"I wanted to show this to you," he said with emotion. "During the few hours we have known each other today we spoke several times about problems that will be of the utmost importance in your lives, and that mean more to our family than you can know. Perhaps you have sensed it already. Because you are the sons of my best friend and—permit me to say so—because I have come to trust you,[190] I think I may give you these writings; you might read them together and return them tomorrow when we visit. This is the diary of my oldest son, Harald; it goes to the day before his death. He died for a just cause—a victim of the abuse of power.[191] It was very hard for us.[192] My wife and—I think I may tell you—Johannes were a great help to the rest of us."

The major looked at his son with an expression of indescribable love.

"Dear boys," he then said to the other three, "I think you will find a good and loyal friend in Johannes, and he a brother in you. We have lived here secluded from all people for a year. Now, after overcoming our bitterness, we must find our way back to people[193] and perhaps, perhaps—you can help our children somewhat in that."

Outside the ringing came to an end. Misericordia, Justitia, Pax— they pealed once more; then it was still. Evening was here.

Documents

[by Klaus Bonhoeffer, December 1926]

Preamble: The Constitution is patriarchal.

ORGANIZATIONAL STRUCTURE

The House of Bonhoeffer is a limited liability company.
Honorary President: Frau von Bonhoeffer[1]
Owner: Privy Councilor Bonhoeffer
Sole Business Manager: Frau Paula Bonhoeffer
The latter may and shall in special cases, if required in her judgment, consult with experts, especially:
Frau Czeppan: as economic counsel
Frau Leibholz: as artistic warden
Fräulein von Hase: as Great Moral Staff
Frau Czerny: as information bureau
Schoolmaster Dr. Czeppan: in political affairs[2]
The Sole Business Manager will decide by herself on medical problems.

The male descendants of the Owner receive half a vote as soon as they have passed the age of thirty.[3] But in important matters, the nonvoting descendants shall also be heard.

The female descendants are expected, before completion of their twenty-first year, to find an opportunity to found a branch company.

The Constitution exists by the grace of God. Motions to change it will be considered blasphemy and will be prosecuted.

CONDUCT IN THE HOUSE

General Rules

Nighttime is to be observed absolutely during the hours from

10:00 P.M. to 6:30 A.M., at which hour the Owner and the Sole Business Manager rise. Noise, loud talking in the cloakrooms and in the stairwells is especially to be avoided.

This rule does not apply to the Owner or to the Sole Business Manager. On the contrary, the latter has the right, at any hour, even during the night, audibly to reproach members of the House with good and sufficient reason for breaking the House rules.

The afternoon hour from 3:00 P.M. to 4:00 P.M. shall also be considered nighttime for the purpose of this rule.

The conduct of the members of the House is regulated by the national Constitution. However, they enjoy special privileges as 1) they have the right to interrupt not only all members of the House, but even the Owner himself, and thus to lead the conversation on to domestic matters; and 2) they have priority over the performance of all remaining persons in the House.

In order to preserve the connection between the headquarters in Grunewald and the branches in Stuttgart and Hamburg,[4] the Sole Business Manager must engage in at least three telephone conversations daily. She also takes charge of the written correspondence. The telephone system with six (6) extensions above all serves the private conversations of the daughters of the House with their girlfriends or with their fiancés. Insofar as this purpose is not infringed upon by so doing, the Owner may also use the telephone system. An interruption of said private conversation by interjection on the part of the Owner shall not be considered an infringement.

Because of her progressive orientation, the care and promotion of the radio is incumbent upon the Honorary President alone. The Owner and the Sole Business Manager shall adopt a wait-and-see attitude toward the radio for the time being, until such time as it is possible for educated society to make a definitive judgment about this innovation.

The Meals

The communal family breakfast takes place at 7:15 A.M. At 11:00 A.M. a meeting of the members takes place over a cup of coffee at headquarters or in the tearoom at A. Wertheim or at Miericke's.[5]

Lunch punctually after four (4) strikes on the gong.
At 4:00 P.M. a light tea is offered. Guests may be brought.
6:20 P.M.: First dinner for concert-goers, and so forth.
7:30 P.M.: Second dinner. Three courses.
10:30 P.M.: Third dinner for hard workers.

THE HOUSE ON WANGENHEIMSTRASSE
FOR MAMA ON HER FIRST BIRTHDAY IN THE NEW HOUSE
[30 December] 1935
by Emmi [Bonhoeffer, née Delbrück]

In the spring of 1916 my father came to the lunch table from his walk one day at noon and said, "A professor and his family are moving into the Budde house; they have one more child than we do!"

Eva Budde had been a schoolmate of Hanni and occasionally I had been taken along to the house, but I always found it cool and uncomfortable there.

I was eleven years old, playing in the garden with Max; we expanded our game with the handwagon to the street and met our father in front of the garden gate. He was greeting a strange couple, bowing low; he was greeted in return with great friendliness, and a few words were exchanged. I don't remember what they talked about, but I observed with interest the strange lady's bearing and manner of speech. She was different from all the women I had seen before. I couldn't have said more at the time, but I can still see myself looking after the impressive figure somewhat abashed and engrossed.

The first contacts between the neighboring families probably occurred between Sabine, Christel, and me on our trips to school together by train to Savigny-Platz, to Mommsen's, and to Wellmann's.

"How was it yesterday at the Bonhoeffers' birthday party?" my father asked us at the table.

"Wonderful," Max and I said, "the mother kept asking questions and whoever was the first to answer correctly would get a piece of candy from a big bag; and we played 'Tip' with chocolate cookies and the mother even played with us!''

My father smiled, enjoying our enthusiasm, but couldn't avoid shaking his head a bit at the un-Prussian version of the game, which we played with pebbles.

Justus, Max, and I were trotting along Wangenheimstrasse with brushed hair and clean clothes to another of the many birthdays. I asked, somewhat anxiously, whether Justus was quite sure that all three of us were really invited again.

"Definitely," he said, "there are a lot of them, too."

The style of the house, basically similar to ours, yet with quite novel elements, attracted us greatly. First we seized upon quite external things. The expression "Moronic!", for example, thrown at one's opponent in a discussion with a certain shrug of the left shoulder, arched eyebrows, and a shaking of one's head to signify incomprehension, was a habit we acquired, and it promised unknown delights.

The great organization of the household was also very interesting. In our house many things happened incidentally and casually; there everything had a system. One person was mending, one person cooking, one person answered the telephone, the floors were always shined, and no one admonished anybody to help dry the dishes in the kitchen today or to rake the garden once again. For sorting potatoes, everybody got a whole chocolate bar! That was quite an experience!

To a considerable degree the differences between the houses had to do with the professions of the fathers.[7] The cared-for look of the downstairs rooms and the discipline at afternoon tea were a consequence of the "office hours." The term "moronic" suggests itself more readily to the psychiatrist than to the historian. The difference showed most distinctly in our upbringing. On my father's high school record it said under comportment: "If he can hold his bold though sound judgment in check, he will go a long way." Our father loved bold judgment in others too, including his children, and was only concerned for its soundness. He would ask and encourage even us younger ones to make judgments that in no way behooved us. Sometimes, for instance, he read us parts of his political correspondence or articles of general human interest and listened to our opinions on the matter; he did correct our facts, but he didn't care at all about the relationship between the one judging and the person or matter being judged. I was thirteen years old when he asked me: "What do you think of the emperor going to Holland?" We found this style generous and encouraging, but later often had to pay for this boldness that our father had consciously cultivated when we were considered immodest.

There were other peculiar sides to our upbringing of which we first became aware in the house at 14 Wangenheimstrasse. For example: We were a large family around the dining table too and each of us also had our friends who usually visited us ten minutes too early at the end of a meal; they "fell into our dessert," so to speak. My father didn't like having our friends walk around the long table and always said to them: "Hello, child, why don't you sit down with Max right away!" The guests did that very modestly and we thought that that was the way it should be. But when Max arrived at the Bonhoeffers' one day during dessert and right away wanted to sit down next to Dietrich, Klaus ostentatiously shook hands with him and then led him to the next person so that he had to go on a tour past all the brothers and sisters, the parents, Fräulein Horn, and so forth.

It was fortunate for us that we could smooth off our first rough edges in a house where we always felt a kindly benevolence that reinforced our self-assurance after such "staggering experiences." Under "Father Bonhoeffer's" piercing gaze from beneath his pushed-up glasses we felt thoroughly exposed—as we confessed to each other once. Everything that was somehow boastful or vain melted away; one felt small but—and this was the special thing— nevertheless understood in a kindly way.

Choral singing of folk songs, which unfortunately happened rarely at our house for technical reasons, but which we loved nevertheless, flourished on Wangenheimstrasse. Here everyone had a strong voice. Dietrich accompanied any song in any key without music and I think even Justus, who was called the "hummer" in school, here experienced the emotional aspect of singing as an essential factor in the cultivation of heart and mind. For me it was an opportunity to express my feelings in a big chorus without being noticed, and this made me very happy. Herder said about folk songs: "Whoever gets little or nothing out of them thereby shows he has nothing in him anyway. Whoever scorns them unfeelingly shows that he is so completely drowned in foreign imitation that the substance of his own nation has become unworthy and unmoving to him. He is a shoot grafted to a foreign tree or a leaf blown by the wind, that is, an ultimate virtuoso of the latest fashion, a thinker."

Often "Mother Bonhoeffer," as we soon called her among ourselves, sang her song by Beethoven, "Wie herrlich leuchtet mir die Natur"; then Ursel her Brahms song, "Dunkel wie dunkel in Wald und in Feld"; Christel sang "Herz, mein Herz, was soll das geben"; and Sabine, "Du Ring an meinem Finger." Ever since, I haven't liked to hear these songs sung by anyone else.

Summer came with walks nearly every evening in a big group: Hans, Christel, Justus, Grete, Sabine, Klaus, and I; later Susi, Max, and Dietrich, occasionally Karl-Friedrich, and later still, Gert.[8] It seems that at Wangenheimstrasse there was a time before which we were supposed to be back (it must have been the period after the revolution). This hour was transgressed regularly. From about Hubertusallee on, Christel began to make energetic pronouncements of "I don't care, I had a lot of fun!" which made clear the fact that she did care about having to account the next day for getting home late. My parents must have thought us very safe in the Bonhoeffers' company; I can't remember, at any rate, that there was ever any talk about when we had come home.

I also remember evenings at that time when we didn't go for a walk, when probably the parents weren't home. At any rate we made an incredible noise and got into a lot of mischief. I can still see Justus, who wasn't able to join in music making, rhythmically rattling a metal tray with forks and spoons while Klaus, wrapped in shawls, danced around the dining table, and Dietrich did a takeoff on modern music on the piano. The other six or eight accompanied this by running around the room singing, whistling, and laughing, and everyone was completely satisfied by the noise alone.

There was a time when we, especially Justus and I, were so enamored of the Bonhoeffers ["ver-bonhoeffert"] that my mother observed, almost sadly, how we did nothing but talk of the Bonhoeffers and want to go to their place. But because she knows the art of self-restraint she always promoted and fostered the contact with Wangenheimstrasse. It was good and useful for us, and that was decisive for her.

Then came the time of the dances: the summer with the garden parties, the winter with the great masked ball. Father Bonhoeffer was standing at the entrance in a servant's uniform and later during the meal mingled with the help, so that Hans called to him, "Hey, bring some gravy, will you!" My father came as a fisherman from Holstein with wooden clogs, a blue linen jacket, and a black cap. I can still see him as if it were yesterday, coming through the dining room door unbidden, without a mask, but so genuine that few recognized him. Bärbel Hildebrandt, as a violinist in a tail coat next to the grand piano, also remained unrecognized for a long time. I had no mask, was very self-conscious, and when I saw Klaus as a ballerina I was hopelessly depressed and embarrassed; Hanni said of him: "How could the Bonhoeffers invite such a vulgar person!" Only when all of the masks were taken off and Klaus asked me to have coffee did my discomfort go away.

Also wonderful were the skits of some assistants who played clowns and who had composed a ditty with the refrain: "Yes, yes, the diagnosis, that is the total therapy!"

There never was just eating and dancing at the parties on Wangenheimstrasse, there was always something happening. All the guests might be suddenly transformed into a school class with Klaus as the teacher, and one might have to recite a Schiller ballad or state the size of the population of Berlin. There was chamber music or one of the guests—Klaus Brandt for instance—sat down at the piano and set newspaper ads or texts from a history book to music. We also loved it when Klaus did his hussy dance with an umbrella and a big couch cover.

The parties given in this house and garden were countless; no one was ever bored—only a snob would be, and that was about the only type of person you wouldn't meet there. We never knew the effort it cost to organize the practical details for these parties. I can only appreciate the art involved in it since I have been married. At the time, though, everything seemed so impromptu that the opinion got about that "It's no bother to Mother Bonhoeffer, you can see that everything runs by itself!" But the stairs and cupboard doors had no illusions about that; they knew how often they creaked before the guests could imagine that everything ran by itself.

Then came the years when one daughter after another was married in the beautiful, heavy bridal gown; I was to wear it too, as I was treated just like a daughter in many respects. This fulfilled a wish that might have been in the longing glance I sent after the strange lady on Wangenheimstrasse in 1916.

New stimuli entered the house with the sons-in-law. All four faculties and the most varied branches of public life were represented now. When all the children became adults, the house on Wangenheimstrasse remained the center; there each reported events from his activities, raised questions encountered in life, exchanged experiences, and honed his judgment or sought to form one. The dining table, circled a thousand times, and the dignified art cabinet can bear witness to that.

I don't feel up to the task of describing the part played in my life by Papa's way of analyzing and answering life's questions; but among all the varied influences shaping me, it played a major role. The three years I lived in the house itself with Klaus only deepened and strengthened the more instinctive impressions of my childhood. I am sure of one thing, and I can say it here without danger of being thought blunt: I shall never cease being grateful with all my heart.

Dietrich Bonhoeffer's Prison Fiction: A Commentary

BY RUTH ZERNER

Self-scrutiny and self-exploration were continuing themes throughout Dietrich Bonhoeffer's life. During his confinement in Tegel
Prison in 1943 and 1944 these preoccupations became intensified
and fostered a unique creativity, recorded in letters, poems, and
literary fragments smuggled out to his family, his fiancée, and his
friend Eberhard Bethge. The fiction Bonhoeffer penned in his jail
cell became a major vehicle of his self-appraisal and self-confrontation, a probing prelude to his final theological formulations.

The family chronicle which he began in prison, first as a drama
and then as a novel, allowed him to retrieve his personal past.
He re-created the familiarity and cultural ambiance of a world lost
to him in Tegel Prison. Characters resembling his close friend, his
fiancée, and members of his family emerge from the pages of his
saga. This aesthetic attempt at recovering both the past and the
inaccessible present undoubtedly nourished Bonhoeffer with a sense
of comfort and security, as well as with a continuity with his previous
self-image. Finding great pleasure in composing this family narrative, Bonhoeffer pursued it eagerly during his first year of imprisonment, prior to his shift to the serious, penetrating, and prophetic
theological speculations of the spring and summer of 1944. Thus his
initial focus on a work of fiction reflected a long-cherished personal
predilection, rather than his response to a professional priority.

On the other hand, Bonhoeffer's short story "Lance Corporal
Berg" represented a direct response to prison conditions and a
desire to bear witness to the indignities and injustices of imprison-

ment. Although he wrote two short stories in prison, one was lost. Only the tale about Berg remains.[1]

Nothing in Dietrich Bonhoeffer's early life or training as a theologian would have led him to anticipate spending two years in a prison cell. Youngest son of one of Germany's leading psychiatrists, he enjoyed a sheltered and comfortable upper-middle-class childhood in Breslau and in Berlin, including pleasant summers spent with his seven siblings at a country home in Friedrichsbrunn. Having pursued university studies in Tübingen, Berlin, and New York, the twenty-six-year-old Bonhoeffer attained the position of student chaplain and lecturer in theology at the University of Berlin by the time Hitler came to power in January 1933.

No city had as decisive an impact upon Bonhoeffer as Berlin; Eberhard Bethge comments: ". . . the vital influence was the complex multiplicity of Berlin; imperial and then republican Berlin, and the Berlin that slowly succumbed to Nazism; liberal and ecclesiastical, conservative Berlin and the Berlin that opened itself to all the winds of the twentieth century; Berlin with its academic and proletarian districts, its concert halls and museums; the Berlin of street brawls and political plots."[2] Vibrant life and lingering death, growth and decay, all marked the culture and politics of this city during Bonhoeffer's young adulthood. Focus of dizzying contradictions and bold experiments, Berlin was the epitome of the Weimar age which, with all its fads and violence, cradled the first truly modern twentieth-century culture. Yet neither the aesthetic, literary modernisms of avant-garde Weimar culture nor its radical politics ever penetrated deeply into the balanced, moderate atmosphere of the Bonhoeffer family and their academic circle.

However, flexibility of thought, experimentation with new ideas and new departures, as well as tolerance for diversity were hallmarks of Dietrich Bonhoeffer's approach, derived from the Berlin intellectual climate and from the secular humanism of his scientist father and family. Bonhoeffer evidenced an openness to the modern discoveries and breakthroughs in the physical sciences as well as an understanding of the modern secular temperament. At the same time Bonhoeffer never abandoned his search for wholeness of life through faith in Jesus Christ. His doctoral dissertation on the nature of the church, *Sanctorum Communio*, combined theology with insights from sociology, the university field most noted for pioneering approaches, breadth of interest, and adventurous personalities in the twenties. Bonhoeffer's deliberate decision to integrate innovative sociological insights rather than traditional historical methodology indicates his receptivity to change and renewal. Although he chose to write his dissertation under Reinhold Seeberg, an outspoken antimodernist and ultranationalist leader of the academic profession, Bonhoeffer was personally repulsed by reactionary politics and, like his family, was immune to the seductions of Nazism. Stirred by a profound commitment to the positive achievements of Germany's past, Bonhoeffer's nationalism, however, had been tempered by a Christian cosmopolitanism and pacifism, nurtured during his first American stay in 1930 and 1931. Extolling the richness and vigor of a life "deeply rooted in the soil of the past," Bonhoeffer in 1944 capsulized for his godson (the firstborn of Renate Bethge, niece of Dietrich Bonhoeffer and wife of his close friend Eberhard) the legacy of the Bonhoeffer family: "The urban middle-class culture embodied in the home of your mother's parents has led to pride in public service, intellectual achievement and leadership, and a deep-rooted sense of duty towards a great heritage and cultural tradition."[3]

In his prison play and novel, Bonhoeffer—in addition to the re-creation of deeply felt life experiences and human relationships—re-created this family setting from which he drew strength and confidence. Bonhoeffer's prison "art"—admittedly an amateur attempt at aesthetic expression—has been compared by one American scholar to the scales and finger exercises through which a pianist prepares for the more serious playing to come later.[4] Yet in spite of the awkward, unpolished quality of his first earnest attempts at narrative writing, the play and novel fragments provide intriguing insights into the emotions, ideals, and unresolved tensions of the man.

Although an ordained minister of Christ, he assumed responsibility for the guilt of plotting tyrannicide. This willingness to bear

141

the burdens of conspiracy against and murder of Adolf Hitler in order to end the senseless slaughter of millions led Bonhoeffer into partnership with a few men of conscience who formed an elite in his country and in his time. Thus, any new perspectives on Bonhoeffer's attitudes, behavior, and imagination help us to understand better the background and characteristics which shaped him as a resister.

Brought into the inner circles of the anti-Nazi resistance by his brother-in-law Hans von Dohnanyi, Bonhoeffer was valued for his ethical decisiveness, calm rationality, and church contacts abroad.[5] Dietrich Bonhoeffer, his brother Klaus, and brother-in-law Rüdiger Schleicher merged harmoniously into the homogeneous grouping of conspirators (composed of upper-middle-class civil servants and politicians, along with military officers from the upper-middle-class and aristocracy, and also including leaders of German socialism) bound by social and personal ties which predated the Hitler era. Arrested and imprisoned because of his involvement in smuggling fourteen Jews into Switzerland, Bonhoeffer, who had served under Dohnanyi as a member of the *Abwehr*, through his family maintained contact in prison with his fellow conspirators on the outside. Although in jail for more than a year preceding the July 20, 1944 assassination attempt, Bonhoeffer was kept apprised of the plans for killing Hitler and removing Nazi leadership.

These resistance plans, despite divergence in tone or emphasis, all advocated comprehensive social and political reforms which went beyond "mere reversion to the past" in the "particular blend of traditional elements and socially Utopian ideas," which were "nonetheless thoroughly conservative in the sense of Karl Mannheim's distinction between conservative and liberal."[6] In his sophisticated analysis of the social views and political plans of the resistance, Hans Mommsen has refused to identify these German resistance plans with the concept "conservative revolution"; rather he views their programs as a "broad current" drawn from Pan-European as well as specifically German thought patterns.[7] Determined to initiate a new beginning in German history, the upper-class resisters espoused a complex mixture of elitism, anti-egalitarianism, and paternalism, blended with a genuine concern for preserving the core of personal human integrity: the autonomy of man in a mass age. Their brand of reform from above left little room for democracy in the Western European sense of the term. But Christian thinkers like Bonhoeffer and members of the Kreisau circle called for a new elite, men of quality, spiritual strength, and leadership, who would be drawn from all social classes.[8] In addition, Bonhoeffer's elitism was modified by a Christian commitment to seeing history "from below, from the perspective of the outcast, the suspects, the mal- treated, the powerless, the oppressed."[9] Despite the willingness to recruit this new elite from all strata of society, the resisters' elitism followed the pattern of political thought Walter Struve has crisply designated as an "open-yet-authoritarian elite," a concept evolved in German middle-class leadership circles since the end of the nine- teenth century.[10] This ideal allowed for an openness of personnel selection, but not of decision making.

Like Bonhoeffer, many of the anti-Hitler conspirators envisioned an organic social order based on Christian principles, which would overcome the effects of secularism and modern mass culture. In their search for a holistic approach to community life, they longed for a harmonious future in which the ordered Christian family would be a model for both public and private life.[11] Bonhoeffer emerged as an able and articulate spokesman for the spiritual and ethical foundations upon which the conspirators hoped to build a new order in Germany, based on a continuity with the best in their past. With them he shared an enforced inactivity in the present. At the beginning of 1943, several months before his imprisonment, Bonhoeffer described his fellow conspirators as a generation "with so little ground under their feet," a phrase which reappeared in his prison drama along with other elitist, Christian concepts common to the conspiracy. In this New Year 1943 memorandum Bonhoeffer speculated:

> One may ask whether there have ever before in human history been people with so little ground under their feet — people to whom every available alternative seemed equally intolerable, repugnant, and futile, who looked beyond all these existing alternatives for the source of their strength so entirely in the past or in the future, and who yet,

without being dreamers, were able to await the success of their cause so quietly and confidently.[12]

For Bonhoeffer himself these words soon became both prophecy and prescription, as he waited in prison—nourished by visions of the past and of the future.

IMPACT OF IMPRISONMENT

Bonhoeffer adapted to prison confinement by using the creative and undoubtedly therapeutic outlet of fiction to regain his past life and to prepare for the future. His aesthetic efforts may be seen as part of the psychic struggle for survival in prison. In the drama, the leitmotif of imminent death dominates. In the novel, Bonhoeffer re-created the upper-middle-class world he had lost through his arrest, as well as his fiancée's world of landed nobility. Therefore, he anticipated in fiction the two most likely alternatives ahead: his marriage to Maria von Wedemeyer after release from prison (an alliance of bourgeoisie and aristocracy) or death through execution by the Nazis or through belligerent bombing. Anyone self-consciously facing impending death usually encounters those moments of emotional intensity and hypersensitivity that are linked to life's boundary experiences. Special insights and perspectives may emerge, often following patterns increasingly familiar to scientists and scholars studying edge-of-death experiences.[13] We know that during "a brief stage of desperate depression" in the first months of imprisonment Bonhoeffer considered suicide. He feared his possible inability to withstand physical torture during Nazi interrogation; such weakness might cause him to betray his fellow conspirators.[14] Although he overcame this temptation to commit suicide, as a prisoner Bonhoeffer sometimes felt as if his "life were more or less over" and as if he had become old before his time.[15] The eminent scientist-philosopher Carl Friedrich von Weizsäcker has confirmed this judgment, seeing in Bonhoeffer's prison writings "the hallmark of the work of a person's last years [*Alterswerk*], the approach of death opening his eyes to see things. . . ."[16] One may speculate, however, that Bonhoeffer's final, incisive theological insights were not only due to his awareness of death ahead. Probably they were also linked to the self-knowledge gained by his long, liberating look backward to his early life via the fictional retrogression of the drama and the novel.

Unlike his earlier youthful and sporadic attempts at play writing for family gatherings and festivals, Bonhoeffer's prison narrative represented, in his own words, "a bold enterprise" which he had "had in mind for a long time."[17] But the crisis experience of imprisonment provided the impetus, time, and opportunity to clarify his emotions and thoughts for this fictional project.

Art and crisis are not unrelated. Moments of literary inspiration are often linked to psychological crisis situations. Thoughtful scholars have suggested that artistic creation may be understood in part as problem-solving behavior.[18] Emotion and reason are intertwined in the consuming crises of creativity. The "cold air of imprisonment"[19] undoubtedly sharpened unresolved tensions both in Bonhoeffer's normally dialectical thought patterns and in potentially conflicting emotional commitments. For him, imprisonment affirmed the validity of one of his favorite scientific maxims: "high tensions produce strong sparks."[20]

In the unsentimental honesty of conscientious analysis and self-confrontation, Bonhoeffer's prison letters reveal the continuing tension between a longing for continuity and an expectation—at times a fear—of change: "This dialogue with the past, the attempt to hold on to it and recover it, and above all, the fear of losing it, is the almost daily accompaniment of my life here. . . . To live on past memories, whether it was yesterday or last year (they soon melt into one), is my ever-recurring duty."[21] Frequently he assures himself and his friend that nothing has changed for either of them.[22] Yet changes had occurred and were still taking place inside and outside his cell. Although Bonhoeffer rejoices that soon after his imprisonment Eberhard Bethge married Renate Schleicher, Dietrich's niece, Bonhoeffer acknowledges the possibility of initial conflict between marriage and friendship.[23] Yet he longs for a continuation of the friendship "in a future lived with a common purpose, even though in changed circumstances."[24] One of the major changes ahead he cannot fully grasp, because for him, his sweetheart Maria *is* the future, consisting "very much of hints" that lie "more on the horizon of hope than in the realm of possession and tangible experience." Therefore Bonhoeffer, consistently oriented to reality rather than to daydreams and speculation, concludes: "I am forced to live from the past."[25] Such memories of the past predominate in his prison fiction, although the narratives also anticipate the future. Longingly he hopes that his family, friend, and fiancée will remain unchanged while he is in jail.

Within the magnetic field generated by the forces of continuity and discontinuity outside the prison walls lurk the changes inevitable inside, part of his "radically new kind of life."[26] Bonhoeffer suggests that one could adjust to physical hardships, "but one doesn't get used to the psychological strain; on the contrary . . . I'm often finding the world nauseating and burdensome."[27] Comparing prisoners to sick people and children, for whom promises should always be kept, Bonhoeffer begins to comprehend what his psychiatrist father calls "prison psychosis."[28] The tensions of an existence precariously poised between life and death undoubtedly exaggerated the struggles within Bonhoeffer's personality: between hope and despair, between constructive and destructive forces, between active and passive responses, between "resistance and submission"[29]—with the latter phrase of Bonhoeffer's serving as the title for the German edition of his prison correspondence. Other polarities that preoccupied Bonhoeffer included the unexpectedly welcome solitude versus the longing for *vita communis* (in marriage and friendship);[30] traditional religious attitudes versus a new "nonreligious" interpretation of the Bible;[31] the *homo religiosus* versus the man of faith.[32] His prison fiction also reveals his concern for the position of secular humanists (similar to members of his family and members of the anti-Nazi conspiracy) in relationship to the Christian faith. Theologian of reality, Bonhoeffer in prison faced a reality both longed for and feared, seemingly stable and yet changing.

To forge in prison a Christianity of creative tensions, while maintaining the sense of proportion which his middle-class upbringing dictated, Bonhoeffer at first avoided theological writing and turned with special pleasure to writing about his personal experiences. Claiming that he could write "more fluently and freely" in such projects, he began with an essay on time, which has unfortunately been lost.[33] Continuing, however, to "enjoy doing free-lance, non-theological writing,"[34] Bonhoeffer, throughout 1943, worked on his draft for a drama, which he then turned into a novel. Three over-riding themes propel the two narratives: stable, ordered middle-class family life as a source of strength and joy; Christianity "rightly understood";[35] and sacrificial death, accepted and potentially trans-forming. Rejoicing in the harmonies of his middle-class German background, he transcends the limitations of this social setting only when he explores the multidimensional Christian "polyphony of life."[36] For Bonhoeffer, God is the *cantus firmus* for the other melodies of life and the source of the freedom reached through death. Bonhoeffer's personal complexity and creativity emerge most clearly in his literary as well as in his theological writings when he pursues the *vita christiana*. Indeed, the unfinished literary exer-cises may have served as the necessary prelude to later theological breakthroughs in the 1944 correspondence.

SOURCES OF FICTIONAL CHARACTERIZATIONS AND THEMES

Consciously taking refuge in writing as "a measure of self-protec-tion," curbing his longings for family and friends, Bonhoeffer chose to write about the life of a family — first as a play and then as a novel "with a good deal of autobiography mixed up in it."[37] After he had "sketched the outlines of a play" in the summer of 1943, he realized that the material was "not suitable for a drama" and he decided to "rewrite it as a story."[38] In November 1943 he summarized the genesis and aims of the project:

I began to write the story of a contemporary middle-class family. The background for this consisted of all our innumerable conversa-tions on the subject, and my own personal experiences; in short, it was to present afresh middle-class life as we know it in our own families, and especially in the light of Christianity. It tells of two families on terms of friendship living in a small town. Their children grow up, and they gradually enter into the responsibilities of official positions, they try to work together for the good of the community as mayor, teacher, pastor, doctor, engineer. You would recognize many familiar features, and you come into it too. But I haven't yet got much further than the beginning, mainly because the repeated false forecasts of

147

my release have made it difficult for me to concentrate. But the work is giving me great pleasure.[39]

The drama introduces characters who reappear in the novel, although the drama takes place at a later point in time, either during or immediately following a war (probably World War I, although possibly World War II). Unmistakably set in twentieth-century Germany, with disabled and wounded soldiers as the leading protagonists, the drama portrays a father and a returned-veteran son who, like Bonhoeffer, lament the modern mass contempt for genuine values like sacrifice, and the corruptions of society and of language which prevent men of good will from uttering the words: freedom, brotherhood, and Germany.[40] Throughout the play Bonhoeffer sounds the leitmotifs of death, sacrifice, elitist ideals, and the dangers of mass culture. Like Bonhoeffer's own father, the father in the drama is a respected medical doctor. Deeply outraged by the mocking of the sacrifice of a disabled soldier, the doctor undoubtedly expresses Dietrich Bonhoeffer's own anger at the mistreatment of the powerless and his bitter frustrations over the inhumanities of Nazi society. In the play both father and son agree that it would be better to be dead than to witness such a scene.[41]

Several characters in the drama convey aspects of Bonhoeffer's complex personality and attitudes. While the middle-class doctor's son, Christoph, most closely resembles Dietrich Bonhoeffer, the Little Brother [Brüderchen] evokes Bonhoeffer's family position as the youngest son. Moreover, the character of Heinrich, a self-educated survivor of a childhood in the slums, considers suicide, just as Bonhoeffer did during his first weeks in prison. Longing for an early death and yet hesitating before pulling the trigger, the shattered and ambivalent Heinrich encounters a stranger who claims to be Death's deputy. This stranger apparently transmits traces either of Bonhoeffer's own experiences or his observations of others in prison. Unjustly condemned to death, the stranger spent four weeks in jail, anticipating imminent execution. Having become one with Death in his prison cell, upon release the stranger could no longer return to normal life; withdrawing from his sweetheart and mother, he rejected all natural affection and saw all of life with the eyes of Death. Was that Bonhoeffer's personal nightmare or one common among his fellow prisoners? We cannot know for certain. Yet Christoph's more positive and constructive attitudes more clearly approximate the dominant strains in Bonhoeffer's personality. Christoph, stricken in war with an incurable ailment likely to destroy his life within a year, insists that one may find in the past a "deep and firm and good" foundation upon which to build the future, rather than relying on the "quicksand of so-called new ideas."[42]

Bonhoeffer's basic optimism and trust in Germany's future is also revealed by the character of Christoph Brake in the novel fragment. Again a doctor's son, the Christoph of "Sunday" (the novel's first chapter) is younger than in the drama and as yet untouched by war. As a teen-ager, however, Christoph Brake already displays an intense love of his country and a mature readiness to accept the reality that Germany includes the weak and decadent as well as the strong and courageous. For him Germany is not primarily things, but people—the unattractive, like the arrogant forester and the corrupted school comrades, as well as the appealing and upright, including the Brake and von Bremer families and their friends. Human relationships, particularly friendship, become the medium through which Christoph seals his commitment to Germany and to sharing this feeling with Renate von Bremer. With a hopeful confidence Christoph concludes that the decadent personalities in Germany need to be under a "good, strong hand to get well."[43]

By means of a story told within the story Bonhoeffer provides a symbolic reconciliation of social classes as well as a perceptive criticism of what he sees as specifically Teutonic temptations to indulge in excessive dreaming and in hostile confrontation. The pole vault episode in the novel teaches both Brake and von Bremer that "the real task in life is" learning to get along with one another "without knocking each other's skulls in."[44] They both came to see that their middle-class and aristocratic homes had given them similar standards of decency and honor. In retrospect Major von

Bremer recalls that each awoke from "the dream that he was alone in the world and that others existed for his purposes," and then the Major extends the dream analogy to include his fellow Germans:

> We Germans tend so easily to miss our grasp on life, not from wickedness, but from dreaming, delight in words, ideas, and feelings. We find it more difficult to get together than others do. We remain individuals who do bloody battle against each other over the slightest differences—or else we surrender totally, submitting completely to the will of a single individual. But both ways sin against life as it really is, and they must fail. Life demands our being together and we find that so very hard.[45]

The critique and ideals of this aristocrat mirror Bonhoeffer's deepest concern: for life together (also the title of one of his earlier books, "the only one," he confided from his prison cell, "that was of concern" to him "at that moment"[46]). One of Bonhoeffer's close church associates has ably conveyed Bonhoeffer's extraordinary sensitivity for human relationships: "It was not only theological or church questions that haunted him, but people troubled him too. With close interest he watched them drawing to one another and then again repulsing each other, and asked himself how this could be and found no answer. And there was also the world before his keen eyes, with its economic, social and cultural phenomena. How true community might come between individual men or groups of men was a question he never solved."[47]

The leitmotifs of Christianity rightly understood, and responsible, cultured middle-class German family life predominate in the novel fragment, with the theme of sacrificial death only alluded to in its closing paragraphs. Bonhoeffer's originality usually lay in his ability to grasp the essentials of the Christian gospel and to apply them to his reality, often in matter-of-fact, nonreligious language. In the novel he attempts to snatch fresh Christian insights from the traditional forms of middle-class life. The narrative form of the novel allows Bonhoeffer to probe the thoughts and personalities of the family members without continually creating the actions and encounters that a drama requires. Yet the Christianity he portrays is essentially one of deeds, not just of words.

Bonhoeffer's respect for consistent Christian convictions and for humane sensibilities appears in the three supportive characters of Ulrich, Renate, and the grandmother. As the indispensable friend of Christoph in the drama and in the novel, Ulrich is modeled on Eberhard Bethge. With his "warm enthusiasm and great perceptiveness,"[48] Ulrich provides support, a source of certain ideas and a clarification of others, as well as a thoughtful critic and challenger when necessary. It is Ulrich who coins the significant term "unconscious Christianity" in response to a query by Christoph in the novel.[49] Like Bonhoeffer's own fiancée, Maria von Wedemeyer, Christoph's aristocratic sweetheart, Renate von Bremer, is a sensitive, thoughtful young woman. Her fictional characterization is, however, ambivalent. In the drama she is a mature, poised woman, whose maturity and understanding exceed that of Ulrich. Providing strong, silent support for the troubled Christoph, she understands the need for wordless communication in a crisis. But the Renate of the novel is younger, less mature, and herself troubled. When she meets Christoph, she is suffering from the pangs of homesickness for South Africa. During the early phase of Bonhoeffer's courtship of Maria she was also troubled, not by homesickness, but by the recent deaths in war of her father and brother. Later, while Bonhoeffer was in prison, Maria revealed a steady strength and good humor which deeply moved him. Thus both aspects of their brief relationship emerge in the fictional sweetheart, Renate.

The opening scenes in both the drama and the novel focus on Christoph's grandmother, modeled in part on Ruth von Kleist-Retzow, a lively, thoughtful Christian dowager (and grandmother of Bonhoeffer's fiancée), and in part on Julie Tafel Bonhoeffer, Dietrich Bonhoeffer's grandmother, a woman of conviction and courage, who was undaunted by a 1933 SA boycott of Jewish stores. Pious but tough, discerning but kind, Frau Brake expresses her Christian faith with simplicity and eloquence. Sharply critical of the babbling, unsubstantial sermon she has heard in church, she reflects that such preaching serves as one more "nail in the coffin of the Christian faith."[50] Just as her words and actions are undoubtedly based on the behavior of the two strong-minded grandmothers of Bonhoeffer and of his fiancée, so the insolent tyranny of the novel's forester [*Gelbstiefel*] is based on an actual occurrence in Bonhoeffer's childhood. The incident took place during a summer vacation at the family country home in Friedrichsbrunn. Christoph's firm and uncompromising response to the forester conveys Bonhoeffer's righteous anger when an innocent or powerless individual is attacked by oppressors.

In "Sunday," the sacrificial death of a young aristocrat, son of Major von Bremer, is only hinted at, never fully explained. But in its impact it resembles the death of Walter Bonhoeffer, an older brother of Dietrich; Walter died as a soldier in World War I. Apparently the fictional death took place while the von Bremers were living on their plantation in South Africa. Bonhoeffer implies that an act of heroism or sacrifice preceded this tragic event. One may speculate that the death was in a noble cause, perhaps linked to the suffering of Blacks in South Africa. Bonhoeffer's passionate interest in the plight of Blacks in America might have motivated his choice of the South African setting as part of the novel's background.[51] Whatever the roots of his images, Bonhoeffer's novel never loses sight of the pressing political and theological issues of community life, pacifist ideals, reconciliation, and sacrificial death.

Concern for those who suffer sacrificially, as well as his concern for corruption and injustice in prison, motivated Bonhoeffer's 1944 short story, "Lance-Corporal Berg," an account of a humane German soldier disfigured on the front lines by a flame thrower. Assigned to military prison guard duty, Berg's honest assessment of the prisoners' psychological and physical needs intimidates the deceitful and guilty prison administrators. A few pointed suggestions about improvements in prisoners' treatment earn Berg an immediate reassignment to the front lines.[52] Like the drama and novel fragments, this short story demonstrates Bonhoeffer's passion to display compassion and to frustrate the petty tyrants who torment those who suffer unjustly or for righteousness' sake.

ARTISTIC REGRESSION AND THEOLOGICAL INSIGHTS

Although the Berg story is based on recent experiences in Tegel Prison, the drama and novel are clear examples of Bonhoeffer's

ability to regress to much earlier episodes. Central to artistic creativity is "a relaxation ('regression') of ego functions"; this aesthetic
regression includes a return to deep emotional springs and at the
same time intellectually "purposive and controlled" attitudes.[53]
A writer like Bonhoeffer struggles to combine "an ability to regress
to the inner sources of conflict (as any artist must) with the ability
to project these sources into an outer world."[54] Bonhoeffer's literary retrieval of past experiences and emotions is most effective
and multidimensional when he projects deeply felt theological
truths in nontheological language. For him God and the past remain intertwined, as evident in his own description of what the
psychologists call regression. Commenting on the poetic biblical
passage about "a time to weep, and a time to laugh . . . and God
seeks again what is past" (Ecclesiastes 3:4, 15), Bonhoeffer explains
the meaning of the last words:

> Nothing that is past is lost . . . God gathers up again with us our past,
> which belongs to us. So when we are seized by a longing for the past —
> and this may happen when we least expect it — we may be sure that
> it is only one of the many "hours" that God is always holding ready
> for us. So we oughtn't to seek the past again by our own efforts,
> but only with God.[55]

Through the Christian faith Bonhoeffer tried to bridge the gaps
between the three rigidly defined classes in his novel. By stressing the affinity between middle-class and aristocratic values on
an elitist, but also Christian basis, he captured the essence of his
immediate circle of anti-Hitler conspirators and suggested a synthesis which foreshadowed his impending marriage into a Junker
family. His entry into that aristocratic family circle had been linked
to Christian commitments and to the Confessing Church struggle.
Indeed Bonhoeffer's attitude towards the scriptures stressed what
could be termed "the aristocratic authority" of the message; he
denounced clerical tricks that were "far too unaristocratic for the
Word of God."[56] Yet at least one student of Bonhoeffer's writings
during the year 1943 has observed "the contradiction between the
Gospel to which he was trying to be true and the authoritarian
structures in which he was trying to live. The Gospel must finally
explode his framework."[57] Although von Bremer, the kindly aristo-

cratic patriarch of the novel, listened indulgently to the younger generation, he already had all the right answers. Undoubtedly, Bonhoeffer's novel conveys a conservative, fixed sense of social roles assigned to each generation and sex, stressing appropriate functions and mutual responsibilities. In the fictional discussions between the two teen-age characters most closely paralleling Bonhoeffer and his friend Bethge, Bonhoeffer touches on the unresolved conflict that obviously troubled him: between the Christian teaching of equality before God epitomized in St. Paul's assertion that in Christ there is neither Jew nor Gentile, slave nor free, man nor woman, since all are one in Christ, and the common-sense conviction that there must be distinctions between the upper and lower levels of society, "that everything depends on the right people being on top."[58] Here Bonhoeffer recognizes that his proposal for a Christian elite to solve social and political problems rests on a shaky theological foundation. He fails to resolve the dilemma.

UNCONSCIOUS CHRISTIANITY

Although the novel fragment lacks profound social or political analysis, it introduces into the corpus of Bonhoeffer's writings a new phrase (which he twice mentions briefly in his later 1944 correspondence): "unconscious Christianity." With deep concern for unassuming, ethically sensitive, nonreligious humanists (like many members of his family and of the anti-Hitler conspiracy), Bonhoeffer allows one of his characters to explain that "without knowing it and in any case without articulating it, they in reality are still living in Christianity, an unconscious Christianity."[59] Claiming that a "Christian instinct" drew him "more to the religionless people than to the religious," Bonhoeffer in his 1944 letters anticipated a "religionless Christianity" and linked this thought with the need to read the New Testament more fully "in the light of the Old."[60] While in prison he speculated tentatively about whether the Ten Commandments represented "a peasant ethic," in contrast to a bourgeois ethic focused on the sin of avoiding "free responsibility."[61] Such comments reveal the degree to which middle-class values and Christian ethics merged in Bonhoeffer's mind. His upper-middle-class background could be both limiting and liberating.

In his prison fiction he attempted to reconcile upper-class and middle-class values, including also selected lower-class types in the synthesis. Through the concept of "unconscious Christianity" he fitted the nonreligious among his family and friends into his Christian world view. Bold in design, the synthesis remained uneasy and fragile. In our post-Holocaust world I wonder whether Christian theologians might not construct a sturdier support for such a synthesis by coining and cultivating the concept of an "unconscious Judaism" shared by both Christians and secularists. Moving beyond Bonhoeffer's inclusion of ethical secularists within the net of "unconscious Christianity," I would suggest that in our time we could extend the concept by recognizing that Bonhoeffer (as well as many Christians and secularists) was in actuality an "unconscious Jew." By pursuing Bonhoeffer's lead in studying Jewish scriptures and traditions in their diversity and multithematic richness, and by not forcing them into Christian taxonomies, "unconscious Judaism" may emerge as a bridge opening the road to deepening Jewish-Christian understanding. Christians may glimpse afresh the deep Jewish roots of their own Christian attitudes and faith. In my opinion, this would not be out of keeping with Bonhoeffer's inclinations.

By admission an advocate of training and discipline, Bonhoeffer evolved in his fiction an image of middle-class life that comes close to a "culture of law"—with stress upon order, justice, stability, legality, lack of sentimentality. Even his concept of grace was disciplined and demanding—"costly grace." In his last letters he began to understand the dangers of this approach, but did not deny it.[62] Instead he effectively transcended it through mental experimentation with other routes to the same goal.

A unique and authoritative model for summarizing the insights of Bonhoeffer's fiction emerges from his poetry. In a few hours of emotional intensity on 21 July 1944, he wrote "Stations on the Road to Freedom," a poem on a subject about which he "felt deeply."[63] It was unquestionably part of Bonhoeffer's response to the shocking news that the July 20th plot against Hitler had failed. Written in the knowledge that his own death was now more likely, that poem is a distillation of his life and thought. By contrast, the narratives of the previous year appear as diffusions or dilutions of personal and professional concerns. Accustomed to personifying abstract concepts, in the poem Bonhoeffer seized his images not from nature but from the realm of ideas: freedom, discipline, action, suffering, death.[64] In a way that may appear paradoxical, discipline remained the indispensable compass and guide for Bonhoeffer's journey to freedom. It was present from the start—in the family upbringing—and continued to control his habits until the climax of death.

DISCIPLINE

Bonhoeffer was upper-middle class by birth and background, but a committed Christian by choice. In both of these realms, however, he emphasized discipline and training: "With me," he wrote to Bethge, "training is almost everything. Without training I would be a quite tedious don!"[65] While in prison he forced himself to follow routines of outer discipline (early rising, exercises, cold showers) to provide "some support" for his inner discipline. He found strength to overcome tension and longing by "looking the longing straight in the face" and by keeping "step with God" and not "pressing on a few steps ahead" or "dawdling a step behind." Bonhoeffer maintained that this capacity to "put up with a long period of tension," without seeking immediate "compensation in short-lived pleasures" was often lacking in the proletarian classes and resulted in "the ruin of all intellectual fertility."[66] He did, however, admire those members of the working class who trained themselves through sustained reading and concentrated thought, including a fellow prisoner whom he considered "by far the most intelligent and attractive" man in the place.[67] Perhaps that prisoner impelled Bonhoeffer to create the character of Heinrich in his drama. A dockworker who chooses to "live with God in the Hell" of a harbor slum, Heinrich is a complex character who reads the Bible as well as sociological and economic treatises, but does not attend church or profess traditional religious piety. Refusing offers of formal university education or professional training, he claims that such striving might cause him to forget God and the misery around him. He displays a secular form of Christlike behavior, comforting, feeding, and ministering to the needs of the poor, especially the children, yet rejecting the role of social reformer or preacher.[68] With this personality, Bonhoeffer seems to be attempting to answer some of the most insistent questions he posed in prison: "How can Christ become the Lord of the religionless as well? Are there religionless Christians?"[69] In Heinrich's life Bonhoeffer seems to be affirming that "it is not the religious act that makes the Christian, but participation in the sufferings of God in the secular life."[70] This is for Bonhoeffer the highest form of discipline—linked to actions for others.

Although Bonhoeffer perceives the possibility of such disciplined living among selected members of the working class, he clearly focuses on the sturdy, cultured discipline, balance, and wholeness of middle-class family life, as well as the virtues of a pious Christian aristocracy, exemplified by the von Bremers in his novel. Yet most of his middle class and aristocratic characters are idealized or heroic types, whereas compelling emotional complexities and contradictions are found in the dockworker, Heinrich. With his compassionate and heroic good works and conscious chastity, Heinrich may also be seen as a type—a secular Christ figure. But Heinrich's insistent longing for death, his despair at having been nursed back to health and life in a military hospital, and his flirtation with suicide betray his inner weaknesses and conflicts, revealing his basic humanity. Probably Heinrich's tensions and contradictory emotional dynamics came closest to representing Bonhoeffer's own inner turmoil during the first months in prison (when he wrestled with the alternative of suicide) and during earlier years when temptations of slothfulness and overwhelming sorrow [accidie and tristitia] plagued him.[71]

The second figure who comes close to representing some of Bonhoeffer's emotional frustrations is the grandmother of the upper-middle-class family, Frau Brake. Although the other women and men in his narrative are clearly stereotypes, playing their assigned social-class roles, she is a dynamic personality, discontented with aspects of the status quo, especially in the church.

Highly acculturated to upper-middle-class academic life, with its habits of order, goals of harmony, balance, simplicity, and rejection of mediocrity, Bonhoeffer was not avant garde in his literary tastes. He admired the simple, lucid style of nineteenth-century realistic novelists like Stifter, Fontane, and Gotthelf and devoured their works in prison.[72] Consciously imitating their narrative style, his approach was at best derivative and hardly original. Stifter's respect for reticence and "refusal to force his way into a man's inner life" impressed Bonhoeffer, who went through a period of disgust with psychology, concluding: "There is something more at stake than self-knowledge."[73] But those nineteenth-century novels tended to reinforce Bonhoeffer's glorification of the life of the German middle class and landed gentry, creating almost a cult of family, friendship, and middle-class virtues. In contrast to Thomas Mann and Hermann Hesse, Bonhoeffer does not expose decay or dissolution in these bourgeois institutions. Throughout his fiction, Bonhoeffer averts his attention from evil and focuses on positive actions and hopeful thoughts, just as his prison reading of Dostoyevsky's *The House of the Dead*, a gripping account of prison life, focuses on the germ of hope rather than on the despair and violence.[74] Bonhoeffer clarifies his ideas with such stark, sharp strokes that his characters often lack a feeling for ambiguity. The dichotomies are etched with an "either/or" type of simplicity which weakens the force of the narrative. Missing is the kind of blending evident in his more elastic theological reflections during the following year: "It's therefore impossible to define the boundary between resistance and submission on abstract principles; but both of them must exist and both of them must be practiced."[75] Yet perhaps the disciplined clarification of thought and character in the drama and novel were necessary preliminaries to the later, more supple theological speculations.

ACTION

Although training was "almost everything"[76] for Bonhoeffer, it inevitably led to an ethic of action. His prison fiction focuses dramatically on the unequivocal need for action against petty tyranny and against the callous disrespect and contempt for less fortunate human beings. This serious moral concern is validated in the drama's defense of a crippled soldier's honor. In the novel's first chapter similar responses appear in the spontaneous reaction against the forester's abuse of power, the frustration of the schoolboys' plot by a substitutionary act, as well as the concluding allusion to an act of sacrifice culminating in death. Inspired by the ethical earnestness of the German novelists Fontane and Reuter, Bonhoeffer maintained that "one often learns more about ethics from such books as these than from textbooks."[77] The ethics taught in his own literary manuscripts flowed from deep emotional wells: "It makes me furious to see quite defenseless people being unjustly shouted at and insulted. These petty tormentors, who can rage like that and whom one finds everywhere, get me worked up for hours on end."[78] Some of the specific frustrations linked with his experiences of prison mismanagement and corruption emerge in the terse tale of Lance-Corporal Berg.

But here, as in the other literary examples explicitly developed by Bonhoeffer, the evils exposed appear commonplace and trivial, reminiscent of Hannah Arendt's phrase, "the banality of evil."[79] Why did Bonhoeffer focus on such comparatively minor instances of evil, when he was surrounded by so many acts of gross evil and inhumanity in Nazi Germany? Since the 1930's his brother-in-law and later his most intimate associate in the conspiracy, Hans von Dohnanyi, had kept a secret file of the Nazi regime's acts of illegality and injustice. Bonhoeffer's ethic allows no easy retreat from reality, but neither in his literary nor his theological writings does he focus on the most gross and revolting examples of evil in modern societies. Why? The question lingers. Part of the answer may lie in his sense of priorities: It is more urgent to take action against evil than to expend energies on the description and analysis of evil itself. Failure to act—the sin of omission—preoccupied him more than the abuse of power in itself. Perhaps he sensed the dangers and temptations inherent in concentrating on the evil, especially in its most repulsive forms. It might have been a matter of taste, an aesthetic avoidance, or perhaps an emotional avoidance. Bonhoeffer's faith demanded an "elasticity of behavior,"[80] looking forward to remedies and not dwelling on evil. For him the most important question for the future was "how we can find a basis for human life together, what spiritual realities and laws we accept as foundations of a meaningful human life."[81]

SUFFERING

Viewing life from the perspective of those who suffer was "an experience of incomparable value" for Bonhoeffer. Despite his literary preoccupation with his own upper-middle-class background, his narratives also provide examples of his interest in viewing life and history "from below, from the perspective of the outcast, the suspects, the maltreated, the powerless, the oppressed, the reviled. . . . We have to learn that personal suffering is a more effective key, a more rewarding principle for exploring the world in thought and action than personal good fortune.[82] Heinrich, the drama's fascinating dockworker-Christ figure, illustrates this concern, as well as do Bonhoeffer's theological admonitions to participate in the suffering and powerlessness of God by "living completely in this world."[83]

In Bonhoeffer's personal life and in his literary imagination, homesickness could be a significant source of suffering. Renate, the sweetheart of the novel's central character, Christoph, longs to return to her father's South African plantation. Although the fictional Christoph responds instinctively to such suffering, Bonhoeffer's later prison letters indicate that he moved to another level of insight concerning the deepest nature of suffering: "No, suffering must be something quite different, and have a quite different dimension, from what I've so far experienced."[84] For Bonhoeffer silence represents a profound way to identify with and to respond to certain instances of suffering—those circumstances in which human action appears useless or irreverent. This is particularly apparent in circumstances of imminent death. At a climactic moment in the drama, when Christoph's sweetheart and best friend both realize that he is suffering from a fatal illness, they express their reactions silently, writing terse requests for forgiveness on slips of paper. Even before this tragic revelation, Renate expresses complete trust in her lover, requiring no explanations from him: "Words in such instances are quite superfluous."[85]

160

DEATH

While only mentioned briefly at the end of the novel's first chapter, death dominates Bonhoeffer's drama, just as it climaxes his poem "Stations on the Road to Freedom," where death is "the greatest of feasts on the journey to freedom eternal."[86] Convinced that the cultured man "must be able to face danger and death,"[87] Bonhoeffer shows in his fiction that the elite know how to die. He did not dwell on evil, but Bonhoeffer examined death without flinching. His most compelling literary images appear in the opening lines of the drama, and they depict death in the tale of a hunter who pursues and lovingly kills his prey:

> GRANDMOTHER (reading): ". . . The hunter had stalked the wonderful animal for many days and weeks. Several times he had had it in his sights, but didn't shoot. He couldn't stop feasting his eyes on the magnificence of this creature. But one evening at sunset it so happened that the animal stepped out of the woods right in front of him, looked at him with very calm eyes, and stood there without fear. Never before had the hunter seen the animal like that. A wild longing seized him to have it, not to give it up, not to let it escape again. He loved the animal so much that he could not part from it anymore. Very slowly he lifted his gun, eye to eye with the animal, a last long glance, a long lingering; then came the shot. Afterward all was very quiet, and the last rays of the evening sun fell reconcilingly and peacefully on the fallen creature and its hunter." (*She closes the book and puts it down*) [then comments to her grandson] . . . The end of the story is not in the book. But it most certainly continues; as a matter of fact, it really begins at this point.[88]

The grandmother's concluding remark is almost identical to the words attributed to Bonhoeffer the day before his execution: "This is the end—for me the beginning of life."[89] Thus in his prison play Bonhoeffer had prepared for and actually rehearsed his death by means of a sensuous, strong story, told in a matter-of-fact style, artlessly blending the triad of themes so dear to German Romanticism: death, love, and beauty. We may assume that God is the hunter and that Bonhoeffer is the creature. Bonhoeffer's emotional attachments to children, storytelling, and the stage[90] combined in this tale which uses nonreligious language and images to communicate

161

traditionally religious themes: God, faith, trust, reconciliation, creation, and re-creation. Bonhoeffer sees his life as a story, and at the end there is a new beginning. God loves and wants the story and the actor. So the life goes back to the author, who is also the director and the spectator.

The characters in Bonhoeffer's drama confront death in its complexity, both in its seductive aura and in its sinister reminders. These encounters emerge first through the transforming lure of a fairy tale, then through the veteran son condemned to death by incurable illness, and finally personified in an ex-prisoner, uncompromising in his assertions about the death-in-life experienced in prison and buried in modern mass culture. The last portion of the novel fragment, however, intimates the unmistakably theological theme of a son's sacrificial death.

COMPARISONS WITH OTHER PRISON EXPERIENCES AND WITH HOLOCAUST LITERATURE

For Bonhoeffer, Tegel Prison provided the opportunity and impetus to continue and to focus on what Bethge calls "his life-long preoccupation with whether and how he would face up to death."[91] Bonhoeffer's exploration of the question of death began in childhood, surfaced in an undated literary fragment which his biographer attributes to the year 1932, and appeared again in his 1939 proposal of the theme "the death in the Christian message" for a series of Edinburgh lectures (never to be delivered due to the outbreak of World War II), and in a 20 September 1939 letter to fellow pastors.[92] The evidence of Bonhoeffer's prison fiction supports the conclusion that his confrontations with the abstract concept of death evolved into a profound personal acceptance of this most likely imminent event. And as Bonhoeffer's prison self-confrontation focused on a struggle with suicide and a final acceptance of death, so other political prisoners have recorded similar wrestling with unresolved or unexamined questions in their own lives.

In his autobiography, Anwar el-Sadat of Egypt writes eloquently of "the liberation of 'self'" that occurred during his two-and-a-half years as a political prisoner:

162

Two places in this world make it impossible for a man to escape from himself: a battlefield and a prison cell. In Cell 54 I could only be my own companion, day and night, and it was only natural that I should come to know that "self" of mine. I had never had such a chance before, preoccupied as I had been with work in the army and with politics, and hurried along by the constant stream of daily life.

Now in the complete solitude of Cell 54, when I had no links at all with the outside world—not even newspapers or a radio—the only way in which I could break my loneliness was, paradoxically, to seek the companionship of that inner entity I call "self." It was not easy. A barrier seemed to stand between us. There were areas of suffering which kept that "self" in the dark, shadows which troubled my mind and accentuated the difficulty of self-confrontation. . . .

Nothing is more important than self-knowledge. Once I had come to know what I wanted, and got rid of what I didn't, I was reconciled to my "self" and learned to live at peace with it.[93]

Like Bonhoeffer, Sadat came to know himself better through personal suffering and through wide-ranging reading in jail.[94]

Intense mental concentration and dedication similar to Bonhoeffer's determination "to hold out in this boundary situation"[95] in prison may be discerned in the prison experience of the American black leader Malcolm X. Reading and studying voraciously in jail, sometimes for as long as fifteen hours a day, he transformed his life. In his autobiography, Malcolm X admits that prison reading "changed forever the course of my life," and he further reflects that prison is "second to college as the best place for a man to go if he needs to do some thinking. If he's *motivated*, in prison he can change his life. . . . Once a man has been to prison, he never looks at himself or at other people the same again."[96]

In prison, Malcolm X overcame the typical prototype associated with children of America's minority groups—evolving the tendency to hold back their thoughts and not to argue with outsiders. The Harvard psychiatrist Robert Coles has provided subtle, sensitive analyses of the variations to be perceived between children of privilege, who learn the art of self-cultivation, knowing how to speak their minds and how to get what they want, and children of the poor and of America's minority groups. Both the rich and the poor children, however, often experience concern and confusion over the social inequality that surrounds them. In many ways Bonhoeffer fits Coles' model for the children of privilege, while Malcolm X grew up as one of Coles' poor, minority group "children of crisis."[97] While in prison, however, both Bonhoeffer and Malcolm X assessed and transcended the limitations of their class backgrounds.

In her pioneering study of the writings of political prisoners of the last two centuries, Bernadette Morand deliberately has excluded literary or imaginative works of political prisoners. Although focusing on writings which describe prison conditions, she signals several themes relevant to Bonhoeffer's prison fiction. Morand maintains that "the urgency of bearing witness and of internal liberation is stronger than any other consideration, even as regards the will to create an aesthetic work."[98] This phenomenon may explain why Bonhoeffer left his fictional project unfinished and turned to theological problems during his last year in prison. But what Morand does not explore is the possibility that aesthetic literary attempts, as in Bonhoeffer's case, may become the passageway leading to an internal liberation, which can free the individual for "a multidimensional life"[99] — even in prison. Indeed, when limited by physical circumstances, one may discover unexpected forms of personal liberation.

Through the literary works he wrote in prison, Bonhoeffer's internal struggle to understand himself (climaxed in the poem "Who Am I?") was transcended and transformed into the theological struggle to understand "who Christ really is, for us today."[100] While Morand tends to identify internal liberation primarily with a "monody" — the compulsion to bear witness[101] — Bonhoeffer's prison writings reveal a more complex polyphony of responses: self-scrutiny and self-confrontation, retrogression and artistic re-creation of past experiences, and the desire to bear witness to suffering. Finally his theological creativity was stimulated, leading to the incisive insights and reflections of his 1944 letters.

In his prison fiction Bonhoeffer also anticipated and paralleled several approaches and conclusions of Jewish survivors. The Jewish writers who lived through or experienced vicariously the Nazi concentration camps share with Bonhoeffer an overwhelming nostalgia for the past, a tendency to idealize their lost world, a readiness to face death and its images and personifications in life, a respect for silence as a response, and the search for a new language. Since the Holocaust many Jews have come to share with Irving Greenberg "an indiscriminate love" of all things Yiddish.[102] A similar indiscriminate love colored Bonhoeffer's fictional re-creation of the life of the German upper-middle class and landed aristocracy. Elie Wiesel has pointed out that the novelists of the Holocaust have described not only the massacres, but also have painted "what preceded it: the life, the peacefulness of the family—the joy of its holidays, the charm of its fools, and the wisdom of its children. They wrote their memoirs so as to bring back to life people and places destroyed by the executioner. And to prove that Jews can—with words—build upon ruins."[103]

On the other hand, interwoven into Nelly Sachs' drama, *Eli: A Mystery Play of the Suffering of Israel*, are visions and voices of killing and death; the fingers of the murderers chant their grim litany.[104] Jewish survivors had to "invent a new language, compose a new rhythm, a new texture to express the ineffable and uncover arts of the secret so jealously guarded by so many dead."[105] Similarly, Bonhoeffer struggled with the desire to communicate the truths of his faith in a new polyphony, in "non-religious language" which would be both "liberating and redeeming."[106] Bonhoeffer's reverence for silence, based in part on the model of his psychiatrist father, also has resonances in Jewish tradition and is a central theme of Wiesel's novel, *The Oath*.[107]

But unlike Bonhoeffer, the Jewish literary intepreters of the Nazi experience had to penetrate the Kingdom of Night, where all they could hope to achieve "was to communicate the impossibility of communication."[108] Survivors like Wiesel had to stare at the evil they had experienced in order to transmit the experience and to transform it. Wiesel, however, waited many years before writing of the terror of Auschwitz. But Bonhoeffer, while waiting in Tegel Prison, had not yet experienced the full sense of national shame and horror to be roused upon the opening of all the Nazi concentration and extermination camps. Bonhoeffer did not live to face in the postwar world the irrepressible implications of the aggregate facts of the Nazi Final Solution. It may be easier to look at one's own death as Bonhoeffer did, than to gaze at overwhelming human evil on a massive scale. Yet Jewish writers have affirmed their humanity while encountering evil in its full reality, not just in its banal reflections.

Bonhoeffer's prison writings, despite their fragmentary character, reinforce the conviction that crisis and creativity are linked. The psyche leads through regression to new insights.[109] The restorative value of his fictional explorations was confirmed by the original, flexible, and challenging theological thinking that followed. His prison narratives introduced the term "unconscious Christianity" and experimented with nonreligious language for such religious concepts as sacrifice and reconciliation. Bonhoeffer groped for a new language for the Christian message, while using the conventional forms of the nineteenth-century realistic novel and of the stage play. He suspected that in the traditional words and acts of the faith there might be "something quite new and revolutionary" though one could not as yet grasp it.[110] In his fiction, and finally in his theological distillations in 1944, he set out to rescue the revolutionary core from what seemed traditional.

Through the literary regression and re-creation of his past life he was freed to transcend the role of an upper-middle-class academic theologian. In prison he overcame the fate of most men and women who live "the life of a biographical type, the 'destiny' of a particular class, rank, or profession."[111] Renouncing the conscious aspirations of an earlier religious desire "to live a holy life, or something like it,"[112] in jail Bonhoeffer traveled the pathways of logical thought and relaxed theological speculations that led to spiritual breakthroughs. Although Bonhoeffer's novel "got stuck"[113] at the beginning of 1944, his fictional writings served as modest but necessary detours in a journey consummated by the fresh, tempting, and transforming theological insights of his spring and summer 1944 correspondence. The uncompleted, less than distinguished narratives of 1943 need not diminish the character and achievements of the man. Rather they expose his humanity and capacity for self-confrontation, for accepting himself, his past, and his death. Dietrich Bonhoeffer remains witness to the fact that to be a disciplined man of the middle—of balanced tensions—need not keep an individual from breaking the trail to a new frontier of thought and of human relations; to be a man of order need not keep one from new and revolutionary experiments and insights.

Dietrich Bonhoeffer's Family

GRANDPARENTS

Friedrich Bonhoeffer (July 16, 1828—January 11, 1907), President of the County Court; *married*
Julie, née Tafel (August 21, 1842—January 13, 1936)
Karl Alfred von Hase (July 12, 1842—January 1, 1914), Court Chaplain and Professor of Theology; *married*
Klara, née Countess von Kalckreuth (October 17, 1851—December 2, 1903)

PARENTS

Karl Bonhoeffer (March 31, 1868—December 4, 1948), Physician, Professor of Psychiatry and Neurology; *married*
Paula, née von Hase (December 30, 1876—February 1, 1951)

BROTHERS AND SISTERS

Karl-Friedrich (January 13, 1899—May 15, 1957), Professor of Physics; *married* Grete, née von Dohnanyi (March 7, 1903—)
Walter (December 10, 1899—April 28, 1918)
Klaus (January 5, 1901—April 23, 1945) Lawyer (Doctor of Jurisprudence); *married* Emmi, née Delbrück (May 15, 1905—)
Ursula (May 21, 1902—); *married* Rüdiger Schleicher (January 14, 1895—April 23, 1945), Professor of Law
    Renate, daughter of Ursula (October 26, 1925—); *married* Eberhard Bethge (August 28, 1909—), Professor of Theology
Christine (October 26, 1903—February 2, 1965); *married* Hans von Dohnanyi (January 1, 1902—April 9, 1945), Lawyer (Doctor of Jurisprudence)

Sabine (February 4, 1906—), Dietrich's twin sister; *married* Gerhard
  Leibholz (November 15, 1901—), Professor of Constitutional
  Law and Political Science, Judge of the Federal Constitutional
  Court
Susanne (August 22, 1909—); *married* Walter Dress (June 18,
  1904—February 6, 1979), Professor of Theology

Abbreviations and Bibliography

Works by and about Bonhoeffer are referred to by the following customary abbreviations. Unless otherwise indicated, the works are by Bonhoeffer.

CF   *Creation and Fall.* London: SCM Press; New York: Macmillan Co.; 1966. Now printed together with *Temptation.*

DB   Bethge, Eberhard. *Dietrich Bonhoeffer: Man of Vision, Man of Courage.* London: William Collins Sons & Co.; New York: Harper & Row, Publishers; 1970. Paperback edition 1977, same pagination.

E   *Ethics.* Edited by Eberhard Bethge. Newly arranged edition. London: William Collins Sons & Co., Fontana Books, 1964; New York: Macmillan Co., paperback, 1965. Pagination differs in 1971 hardcover edition by SCM Press.

GS   *Gesammelte Schriften.* Edited by Eberhard Bethge. Munich: Chr. Kaiser Verlag; vols. 1–4, 2d ed., 1956–66; vols. 5–6, 1972–74.

IKDB   Wolf-Dieter Zimmermann and Ronald Gregor Smith, eds. *I Knew Dietrich Bonhoeffer.* London: William Collins Sons & Co.; New York: Harper & Row, Publishers; 1966. Paperback edition, with same pagination, by William Collins Sons & Co., London, 1973, and William Collins & World Publishing Co., Cleveland, 1977.

LPP   *Letters and Papers from Prison.* Edited by Eberhard Bethge. Enlarged ed., paperback. London: SCM Press, 1971; New York: Macmillan Co., 1972.

NRS   *No Rusty Swords.* Rev. ed., paperback. London: William Collins Sons & Co., 1970; Cleveland: William Collins & World Publishing Co., 1977.

TP   *True Patriotism*. London: William Collins Sons & Co.; New York: Harper & Row, Publishers; 1973.

WF   *The Way to Freedom*. London: William Collins Sons & Co.; New York: Harper & Row, Publishers, 1966. Paperback edition, with same pagination, by William Collins Sons & Co., London, 1972, and William Collins & World Publishing Co., Cleveland, 1977.

(*NRS, TP,* and *WF* are "letters, lectures, and notes," 1928 to 1945, "from the collected works [*Gesammelte Schriften*]" of Dietrich Bonhoeffer, edited and introduced by Edwin H. Robertson.)

Notes

INTRODUCTION TO THE ENGLISH EDITION

1. Particularly important are the supplementary fifth and sixth volumes of the *GS* (1972–74), which contain much valuable material, including some extensive papers and lectures; these publications, however, chiefly appeal to the specialist. Excerpts from the present work first appeared in *GS* 3 (1960), pp. 487–512; they were translated in *TP*, pp. 197–215, 220–35.

2. See *DB*.

3. Eberhard and Renate Bethge, *Costly Grace: An Illustrated Introduction to Dietrich Bonhoeffer* (New York: Harper & Row, Publishers, 1979); published in Britain under the title *Bonhoeffer: An Illustrated Introduction* (London: William Collins Sons & Co., Fount Paperbacks, 1979). An international Bonhoeffer bibliography is in preparation. At present the most complete bibliography of materials in English by and about Bonhoeffer is Clifford Green, "Bonhoeffer Bibliography: English Language Sources," *Union Seminary Quarterly Review* 31 (1976): 227–60; supplements appear periodically in the *Newsletter* of the Bonhoeffer Society.

4. *LPP*, p. 40.

5. To Eberhard Bethge, November 18, 1943; *LPP*, pp. 129–30.

6. *LPP*, pp. 39, 50, 54, 129. While the essay itself is lost, I am confident that the notes for it survive: see *LPP*, pp. 33ff.

7. *LPP*, p. 165.

8. *LPP*, pp. 166ff., esp. pp. 169–70.

9. *LPP*, pp. 94, 200.

10. See below, p. 3.

11. Hence "fiction" in the title of this book is used not as a strict literary category but to refer to the form of the pieces and to distinguish them from Bonhoeffer's *theological* prison writings — albeit in the form of letters! The title of the German original, *Fragmente aus Tegel* (Munich: Chr. Kaiser Verlag, 1978), highlights the incomplete character of these two literary efforts.

12. See Eberhard Bethge in *DB*, e.g., pp. 98, 103, 375ff., 470–471; see also his "Turning Points in Bonhoeffer's Life and Thought," *Union Seminary Quarterly Review* 23 (1967): 3–21. For an exploration of the interplay of theology and autobiography in Bonhoeffer see Clifford Green, *Bonhoeffer: The Sociality of Christ and Humanity* (Missoula, Mont.: Scholars Press, 1975), esp. chap. 4; idem, "Bonhoeffer in the Context of Erikson's

Luther Study" in *Psychohistory and Religion*, ed. Roger A. Johnson (Philadelphia: Fortress Press, 1977), pp. 162–96.

13. See, inter alia, Larry Rasmussen, *Dietrich Bonhoeffer: Reality and Resistance* (Nashville: Abingdon Press, 1972), and Thomas I. Day, "Conviviality and Common Sense: The Meaning of Christian Community for Dietrich Bonhoeffer" (Ph.D. diss., Union Theological Seminary, New York, 1975).

14. See Ruth Zerner, below, p. 154; the second quotation is a citation from Bonhoeffer himself: novel fragment, below, p. 77.

15. In addition to the comments found below in the Bethge Introduction, see also the paper by Renate Bethge given at the 1980 Oxford conference of the Bonhoeffer Society: " 'Elite' and 'Silence' in Bonhoeffer's Person and Thought," in *Ethical Responsibility: Bonhoeffer's Legacy to the Churches*, ed. Geffrey B. Kelly and John D. Godsey (New York: Edwin Mellen Press, 1981), pp. 293–306.

16. See p. 2 above.

17. *"Regression und Kreativität. Ein Nachwort."* See especially nn. 18, 53, 54, 109, and 111 to "Dietrich Bonhoeffer's Prison Fiction: A Commentary," where Zerner refers to the work of Ernst Kris and others (pp. 139ff.).

18. See n. 73 to the novel fragment, p. 188 below.

19. See n. 145 to the novel fragment, p. 194 below.

INTRODUCTION

1. See also the forewords to *GS* 5 and 6, esp. *GS* 5, pp. 8–9, and *GS* 6, pp. 10–11, and also the "Preface to the New Edition" of the *Letters, LPP*, pp. vii–viii.

2. *GS* 3, pp. 478–95; *TP*, pp. 197–215.

3. *GS* 3, pp. 496–512; *TP*, pp. 220–35.

4. Letter of 30 March 1976 from Walther Killy to E. Bethge.

5. In *Het einde van der religie* (Baarn, 1970), p. 190, J. Sperna Weiland, the Dutch scholar, writes that "Christoph is a Christian Nietzsche."

6. *LPP*, p. 71, translation altered.

7. Ruth Zerner, pp. 144 & 155 above.

8. P. 149 above.

9. P. 153 above.

10. Ibid.

11. *E*, pp. 186–87.

12. *LPP*, pp. 129–30.

13. Novel fragment, p. 100.

14. Novel fragment, p. 58.

15. Pp. 139 & 164 above.

16. *E*, pp. 186–87.

17. Zerner, p. 164 above.
18. *LPP*, p. 311.
19. Zerner, p. 155 above.
20. P. 159 above.
21. P. 165–66 above.
22. Novel fragment, p. 82.
23. Novel fragment, p. 85.
24. Novel fragment, p. 87.
25. *LPP*, pp. 94, 129–30.
26. *LPP*, pp. 70, 76, 80, 89, 93, 96, 100, 104, 108.
27. *LPP*, pp. 41ff.
28. *LPP*, pp. 56ff., esp. pp. 64ff. and 67ff. (the latter 2 August 1943).
29. *LPP*, p. 94.
30. Drama fragment, p. 13.
31. Notes to drama fragment, p. 180, n. 32.

DRAMA

1. See the work, written in Tegel, "What is Meant by 'Telling the Truth'?" *E*, pp. 363–72; *LPP*, pp. 130, 158–59, 163.

2. Cf. the report of Bonhoeffer's twin sister, Sabine Leibholz, about his childhood; *IKDB*, pp. 23–24.

3. On names in the family, see the Introduction, above, pp. 5–6, and the novel fragment, n. 1 below. For Bonhoeffer's relationship with his grandmother, Julie Bonhoeffer, née Tafel, see his eulogy for her, *GS* 4, pp. 456ff.

4. Bonhoeffer had encountered the world of hunting in his childhood while vacationing in the summer houses at Wölfelsgrund and Friedrichsbrunn. It reappeared when, before and during the Second World War, he spent many weeks on estates in Pomerania, especially those of the von Kleists.

5. Marginal note: Alteration? more in the style of a fairy tale.

6. The suicide of the cousin Wolf, Count von Kalckreuth, during his military service in 1906 (Rilke dedicated the centerpiece of his trilogy "Requiem" to him) preoccupied the Bonhoeffer children for a long time and always remained full of obscure riddles for them; see the novel, pp. 87–88, and n. 191 to the novel. A copy of a picture of the cousin as a boy (painted by Wolf's father, Leopold, Count von Kalckreuth) hung in one of the rooms of the Friedrichsbrunn house, so that the brothers and sisters always saw it there. About Dietrich's brother Walter, who had been killed in France in 1918, Karl Bonhoeffer wrote: "In our little summer house in the Harz Mountains, he was usually in the woods at sunrise. He knew all the birds and was able to call them. A passionate hunter, he made friends

with the foresters wherever he was and early on became an excellent shot. I witnessed him shooting a circling falcon. But when the bird fell down dead in front of him he was so shaken that he burst into tears. . . . His love of the forest made him consider studying forestry later on. Whether he would have stuck to that I don't know" (from his informal memoir, "Lebens-erinnerungen von Karl Bonhoeffer geschrieben für die Familie," in *Karl Bonhoeffer zum Hundertsten Geburtstag am 31 März 1968*, ed. J. Zutt, H. Straus, and H. Scheller [Berlin: Springer Verlag, 1969], p. 91).

Cf. also the conversation about the death of a bird in the novel, pp. 66ff. above. For the motif of death, see: "He liked thinking about death," *DB*, pp. 24–25; also the report about their childhood by Sabine Leibholz in *IKDB*, pp. 23–24; further, the statement about his own death in *Begegnungen mit Dietrich Bonhoeffer*, ed. Wolf-Dieter Zimmerman (Munich: Chr. Kaiser Verlag, 1964), p. 6. The theme for the Edinburgh Croall Lectures (see *DB*, p. 565) in the winter of 1939–40 was supposed to be "Death in the Christian Message," but in Bloestau in the summer of 1940 there were only Bible studies about death; see also the arguments about death from outside and inside in the Finkenwalde Newsletters, *WF*, pp. 254–55; *GS* 2, pp. 559–60.

7. Marginal note: Fear and foreboding must be more apparent.

8. Deleted: And you might as well admit it, is it surprising, when you look at Christoph?

9. Marginal note: Disappointment, distrust, . . .

10. Marginal note: You see our house, yes *our* house . . . we too were worried when little Anna died (to be developed!). Who knows how long our house. . . . But the world outside, Anna

11. Marginal note: Better to be dead, at least for us old ones and perhaps for the young too, especially for the young.

12. Marginal note: But perhaps it's good for him that way, and for all of us.

13. Marginal note: Not Mother, either, nor Ulrich, nor Renate—my God, poor Renate, what will become of her?

14. Cf. "The Structure of Responsible Life," *E*, pp. 250–51; cf. also the statements about an exaggerated concept of freedom in the novel, pp. 124–25 above.

15. Deleted: A few said one must not say such things anymore and that they would exclude me from the club if I insisted on them. Marginal note: But . . . [illegible] warmth!

16. Deleted: What dangerous matters you discuss there

17. The pianist Dietrich Bonhoeffer, who grew up mainly with the piano literature of the great classical composers, had attended the Kassel Music Days in the autumn of 1938 together with Eberhard Bethge. Subsequently they bought first a clavichord, then a table harpsichord (spinettino), and

also music, especially by Carl Philipp Emanuel Bach, and a 1925 reprint of his *Essay on the True Art of Playing Keyboard Instruments* (1759). The piece mentioned here is usually known to English-speaking musicians as "Farewell to my beloved Silbermann clavichord."

18. Cf. *LPP*, p. 129.

19. Marginal note: Conversation with his girlfriend [crossed out].

20. Possibly a reminiscence of his reading of Dostoevsky's *The Idiot*.

21. Matt. 15:32 and 21:31.

22. Marginal note: No ambition to act!

23. Marginal note: War, liberation, history! and once more this misery with God's servant as a . . . [illegible]

24. Cf. *DB*, p. 387, 259, and *GS* 5, p. 589.

25. Deleted:

Christoph, actually I came to ask your forgiveness because of last night. I know I didn't understand you; I am sorry.

CHRISTOPH: Renate, don't say that. It isn't your fault, I swear it. I can't take that coming from you.

RENATE: I am going, Christoph.

26. Deleted: You were lying next to me in the hospital. I could rely on you. In my hours of weakness you helped me, I held on to you. Very quietly, you made the greatest sacrifice for me.

27. Deleted: we cannot discover

28. Deleted: Oh, of course I will go, Renate. That goes without saying. I couldn't let him go alone; I couldn't bear that at all. But whether I would treat him as gently and patiently as you imagine, I can't promise you. Renate, we'll both, each in our own way, be present for Christoph, as you are able to be.

29. Deleted: for a big lecture he is supposed to give to our club; I think it's going to turn into a book

30. Cf. *LPP*, p. 163: "I sometimes feel as if my life was more or less over, and as if all I had to do now were to finish my *Ethics*."

31. There are two preliminary drafts for this passage:

A. Penciled sketch on thin copy paper (like the sketch of characters and scenes for the drama):

Germany—much misused, now difficult to say. Word that we used self-evidently—has been turned into an empty phrase. Don't love it because someone preaches it at us in newspapers and at rallies, but because it is natural for us. We have to keep silence concerning the highest principles, our great values. [Deleted: hardly one as] Any word about honor, freedom, love of people [*Volk*], comradeship was harder to say for us than it was for the rootless [?] because we lived with them every day, because we experienced their value and their limits. But we won't let the cynics frighten [?] us, either. You know the derivation of the word *cynics*, from the dogs that

177

shamelessly do their dirty business before everyone's eyes. We [deleted: don't need to] smile about these attempts.

The difference is that they could cost us our heads, while for them they are profitable. [Deleted: They are hard times for the well-meaning in which] It is not a good sign if what has always been the calm and firm inner [deleted: and self-evident, tacit] possession and self-evident attitude of all well-meaning people in the country [deleted: becomes a hawker's cry in the marketplace] is yelled out as wisdom outside in the marketplace. [Deleted: The supposedly pure. Still, when the supposedly pure, the . . . (illegible). The slogans of the revolution have never been new. The guardians of the true values turn away in disgust.] Those who [deleted: were] are the guardians of true values, guarding them with their lives, their work, their homes [deleted: who over many generations], will always turn away in disgust from the ringing rhetoric with which one [deleted: stirs to rebellion] flatters those who are ever lacking in spirit and deed. [Deleted: He who has staked his life on the highest values, for him they are . . . One does great things because one can't help it, or else one doesn't do them. There are two kinds of people: those] *Freedom*, who may pronounce the word? [Deleted: other than . . . (illegible)] only of the majesty of law and discipline.

The great words of mankind are sanctuaries which only the humble and faithful may approach. They don't belong on the street. Let us honor the highest goods by silence. Let us learn at last to do what is just without big words, not to profane the sanctuaries.

Not birth or success but humility alone has the right to approach the highest values. The nobility of humility and of faith, of sacrifice, the nobility of dying.

I speak to you in order to protect the great words from misuse. They belong not in the mouths of the masses but in the hearts of the few who guard them with their lives.

Marginal notes on the same sheet of paper:
Trust—doesn't mean knowing everything about one another but
Still more important than frankness is being open for the other, to his silence too; and trust doesn't rest on one's [deleted: having to know] knowing everything about another but on believing in the other.

B. Draft in ink on half a sheet of square-lined letter-pad paper (as used in June of 1943; see Introduction, pp. 10–11):
I am speaking to you to protect from misuse the great words [deleted:

178

which alone (?)] given to mankind. [Deleted: Every (?)] They don't belong in the mouths of the masses but in the hearts of the few who guard
and protect them with their lives. It is never a good sign when what has
always been the calm and firm possession, the unquestioned attitude, of the
well-meaning people in the country is loudly hawked in [deleted: in the
marketplace] the streets as the very latest wisdom. Those who are guardians
[deleted: of the last] of genuine values with their lives, with their work,
and with their homes turn in disgust from the ringing rhetoric that is supposed to turn the masses into prophets. What well-meaning person [deleted:
dares] can still [deleted: pronounce, articulate] utter the degraded words
freedom, brotherhood—and even *Germany?* He seeks them in the quietness of the sanctuary which only the humble and faithful may approach.
Each of us has risked his life for these values; those who use them today
want to profit from them. Let us honor the highest values by silence for a
time, let us learn to do what is just without words for a while. Around
the quiet sanctuary of the lofty words, a new nobility will and must form
in our time. Neither birth nor success will be the basis for this nobility,
but humility, faith, and sacrifice. There is an infallible measure for the great
and the small, for the valid and the inconsequential, for the genuine and
the spurious; that is death. He who is near death is decisive, but he is
also silent. Without words, yes, not understood if need be, he does what
is necessary and just . . ."

Here he stops. I didn't know this paragraph, strange—here is an addition
in pencil:

"Aren't these also merely big words? Hadn't I also better keep silent about
it? How [deleted: how easy it is to write it and how] difficult—to do it.
Renate, Ulrich! Must simply do what is just [and] necessary without words,
not understood—[deleted: Oh, Renate and] Renate, Ulrich—why may I
not tell you?"

ULRICH: Renate, do you understand it?
RENATE: Yes, I think so.
ULRICH: Forgive me, Renate, I didn't know, you are right. God, it isn't
possible.
RENATE: Let it be, Ulrich, it [deleted: must] had to happen this way. We'll
go. Let us leave a note for Christoph.

(*Both write, put it on the table.*)

RENATE: Come, Ulrich, (*Leave very quietly.*) After a while [deleted: Chris-
toph] Little Brother comes [deleted: . . . (illegible) goes, sees] notices the

179

note. (*Reads.*) "Christoph, we were here. Forgive me. Renate. Christoph, I am going to the mountains with you. Ulrich."

This text was then included in the manuscript, with a few corrections but with only one sentence deleted in this section.

32. Cf. the last section of the baptismal letter, *LPP*, pp. 299–300, and "Stations on the Road to Freedom," *LPP*, pp. 370–71. There is an echo here of a kind of secular, political dimension of the "arcane discipline"; cf. *LPP*, pp. 281, 286, 299–300.

33. Deleted: to do silently what must be done

34. In *Het einde van der religie* (Baarn, 1970), J. Sperna Weiland gives an interesting pointer: "it is possible that Bonhoeffer is thinking here of the stranger in the choral pieces of T. S. Eliot's *The Rock*, a play which was performed in London in 1934 (that is, in the year of Bonhoeffer's stay there)." On German stages, surrealist scenes (e.g., the figure of Death in street dress) as well as the language of understatement came into use only after 1945.

35. Deleted: I still have some urgent work to do tonight

36. See n. 6 above. Deleted: But, you don't actually look like that!

37. Deleted: So, you consider yourself, as it were, an agent of Death. That is certainly worth the trouble of listening to.

38. Deleted: It didn't frighten me at all, rather it calmed me down. I tell you, Death is a gentleman quite . . . [illegible]. We talked for a long time. Finally I got my commission from him.
HEINRICH: Madness!

39. For the following dialogue, there is a first version, later deleted:
STRANGER: Not as awful as you think. It left me quite detached from everything. Nothing could excite me, upset me; on the contrary, I felt as calm, as empty and solemn as one does in a cemetery. Only one thing surprised me, I could even say amused me: the blindness of people to their death. I heard them talk, preach, philosophize about their death and make jokes about it; but I see that they really have no idea of it. For death in general, death in philosophy, in sermons, in songs and poetry, isn't interesting at all. What is really interesting is simply my death, your death, with its when, how, and where, and precisely that death they don't know; and therefore they live, all of them without exception, the philosopher and the wit, as though death didn't exist for them. They philosophize, and so they joke, eat, drink, get engaged, married, and they work and labor as if it were for eternity, and while they are doing all of that, someone is looking over their shoulders of whom they [know] nothing. . . .
HEINRICH: So you are saying that you have "second sight"?
STRANGER: Yes and no; for I have lost the first, I only have the "second"

left. Therefore I don't suffer from it like those who are only occasionally overcome and frightened by second sight. It has become second nature for me, and I can't help saying that I feel perfectly comfortable with it. Of course, I no longer have any passions, no stirrings of the heart—the heart ticks as regularly as clockwork—no love, no friendship, no sympathy, no tears—I see only Death everywhere. He is my only acquaintance.

HEINRICH: Quite monotonous, in any case.

STRANGER: On the contrary, young man, quite the contrary, it's extraordinarily diverse and varied. Look here, your case for instance is really interesting and exciting. You are one of the half-people, the wounded. You know more than most, you know your death. But then you make the same grave mistake the others make too; you suddenly take with deadly seriousness everything you do and think; you struggle, writhe, protest. You feel fatally insulted that Death is different from the way you had pictured it. You want to order Death around; you reproach him for avoiding you when you were searching him out and for searching you out now that you are avoiding him. You are making a grand play with the revolver, philosophizing about which would be the "most honorable departure" for you. You would like Death to tickle your vanity a bit. So it goes back and forth and you get nowhere. Young man, I have confidence in you; therefore I want to tell you a secret: for me death is a matter of business, and I have come here to invite you to participate in this business; I live on death, so to speak.

HEINRICH: I warn you, don't come too close to me. But keep talking!

40. Matt. 6:24.

41. Deleted: Look at those people—what do they enjoy?

42. Wisd. of Sol. 1:16.

43. For the connection between death and "the 'They'" ("*das 'Man'*"), see Bonhoeffer's discussion of Heidegger in *Act and Being* (New York: Harper & Row, Publishers, 1961), p. 61 etc.

44. The following section deleted:

Today people don't want to live anymore, they want to disintegrate, die, and for that no laws and no orders are needed; for that a few slogans such as freedom, equal rights, joy of living, and so on suffice, and everything runs its necessary course all by itself. I tell you, it's an incomparable time for people like us. One has to recognize it and know how to exploit it. Do you understand me, young man? Let the others who know nothing philosophize, preach, joke about death, and let the philosopher and the wit have their pleasure; you know more, you don't need that. You must act, you must live on death. That is what I wanted to tell you. (*Rising*) Now I'll leave you hoping that your next visitor doesn't turn your head again. Good evening.

(*As he exits Christoph enters. Heinrich is startled and confused*).

CHRISTOPH: (*Watches the stranger for a moment, then still standing at the door says to Heinrich*): Who was he?

HEINRICH: A shady character.

CHRISTOPH: I have seen him several times already.

HEINRICH: He came into the room unannounced; I don't know him.

CHRISTOPH: I am coming unannounced too, but we know each other, don't we?

HEINRICH: Only very distantly.

45. Deleted: People no longer want simply to live — as

46. Deleted: You can't imagine at all

47. Deleted: whether it might not be importunate

48. Deleted: It could happen after all that

49. Deleted first version of the following dialogue:

HEINRICH: Man to man — you always say that when you want to silence the voice you find troublesome; when you want to rip us out of the community of the common people in which alone we are something; and you know exactly that you needn't fear us any longer once you confront us as individuals. Man to man? That's precisely the point! Let us become men first, then we'll talk with you man to man.

CHRISTOPH: You are very mistaken. This way we'll never get anywhere. You just want to switch the parts, that is all. We can only talk man to man when we again accept the unselfconscious word and the spontaneous deed of the other without suspicion. Nothing is more destructive than to want to examine every word and every deed of the other for its motivations. This eternal psychologizing, analyzing — and whatever else one may call it — means the destruction of all trust, all unselfconsciousness and naturalness; it is the public defamation of all that is decent; it is the revolt of all that is vulgar against what is free and genuine. Men don't exist to look into the abysses of each other's hearts — they shall confidently leave that to God — but they should encounter each other and accept the other as he is, simply, unselfconsciously, with courageous trust.

HEINRICH: And if all your experiences point in the opposite direction?

CHRISTOPH: A man's experiences are like the man himself. The distrustful person will never experience trust, the ungrateful gratitude, the wicked purity; for he will not believe in it. Of course, there are disappointments and bad experiences, but greater than all experiences is faith; for only faith builds up.

HEINRICH: Not everybody can afford to have faith.

CHRISTOPH: You should say, not everybody is called upon to build up. That would be more correct. But that too is only half true. Heinrich, you were in the war as I was. We could have met in a shell crater; be honest, would you have talked to me then the same way?

HEINRICH: No, not then.

50. Deleted: Man to man—you say and that sounds so nice and wise, but you don't notice at all how much contempt you express for us with this expression of esteem.

51. Here follows a second deleted version:

It is true that our backgrounds are very different. I come from a so-called good home, that is, from an old, distinguished, upper-middle-class family. That is a world you don't know. It isn't easy to get to know, either; one must live in it; one must gradually grow into it. Therefore one actually can't talk about it at all. The essential is precisely in [illegible] loosely, naturally, candidly being what one has become. Such a patrician family does not live according to externals but completely from the internal. Without written laws life moves within orders that have grown organically. Everyone has his place, and there is no mistake about it and above all no distrust. Each leaves the other his freedom on a basis of trust. A distrustful person seems vulgar to us. Because we know that our lives are safe in our family, yes, because our home is like a fortress for us in which we always find refuge, therefore we easily appear proud, cynical. But believe me, where respect for what has developed and what is given is our most important and enduring part of life, there trust and respect for the human being grow. To be sure, one should not demand that we blind ourselves to the differences between people. We differentiate between the genuine and the false, the noble and the common, decency and baseness, truth and empty words, content and façade, and (*passionately*) we will let no one forbid us to do so.

HEINRICH: And what is genuine, noble, decent, you believe you know for sure. That is completely self-evident for you, something unquestioned, isn't it?

CHRISTOPH: There must be self-evident things in life, and one must have the courage to uphold them. One can't begin life anew every day by calling into question again everything one has heard, learned, and gained. Many generations have tested the things we take for granted, they have proved themselves in life hundreds and thousands of times.

HEINRICH: Yes, in the lives of your grandfathers; but times change.

CHRISTOPH: But people don't change, at least not in their essential relations. Marriage remains marriage, friendship friendship, loyalty loyalty, treachery treachery. That is just the great mistake, that you always act as though the world began only today and only with you, that you therefore question everything and thus never get around to contributing a brick to the whole.

HEINRICH: What good are bricks when the foundation has cracked?

CHRISTOPH: You talk the way your newspaper reads, and yet you know better. [Deleted: the foundation has been put down and you are the ones who try] They do nothing but drill and drill relentlessly into the foundation, and then they cry with horror and indignation, The foundation has cracked! I tell you, the foundation of our people [?] and our life is deep and firm and good. [Deleted: A thousand years of history let themselves] One need only go on building on it and not on the quicksand of the so-called new ideas.

HEINRICH: You mustn't believe that we are interested in the new ideas—like the literati—that we have the time and desire to want to be original under all circumstances with this . . . [illegible]. Whether old or new ideas, what do we care? We want a life that is worth living—that is all.

52. Concerning home and upper-middle-class family, cf. the corresponding passage in the baptismal letter, *LPP*, pp. 294ff. The description of his parents' house also enters into the poem "Powers of Good," *LPP*, pp. 400–401.

53. Deleted: We want to live—and we can't.

54. Cf. "After Ten Years," esp. the section "No ground under our feet," *LPP*, pp. 3–4. The statement from a fellow soldier of his brother Karl-Friedrich, "What fatherland—my father has no land!" might echo in this passage; this saying impressed the family deeply.

55. Cf. *NRS*, p. 43, and *GS* 5, pp. 467–68, Barcelona 1928–29. Deleted: lost his strength when Hercules . . . him from the ground

56. Deleted: to do us a service and come closer to us by that

57. Deleted: and you must reckon with it every day!

NOVEL

1. In this character there are traits of the grandmother Julie Bonhoeffer née Tafel and of Frau Ruth von Kleist-Retzow of Klein-Krössin in Outer Pomerania (cf. *DB*, pp. 358–59, and *passim*, esp. pp. 506, 509, and 609; see also the German edition of the biography, p. 28), as well as of his own mother. The image of Julie Bonhoeffer dominates as the alert and critical head of the upper-middle-class academic townhouse, that of Ruth von Kleist-Retzow as the ecclesiastical-theological critic of the Sunday service and as the knowledgeable gardener.

2. First Bonhoeffer wrote here "an alderman at the time," then "councillor" in other places, but he then decided on the designation "mayor."

3. From family experience Bonhoeffer himself was accustomed to letting Sunday be a day of rest, and he tried to get the Finkenwalde candidates to shift from working at their desks to playing games, reading, and making music. He was especially impressed once when the von Kleists at Kieckow,

despite a rainy harvesting season, did not order the carts out to bring in the harvest on a dry Sunday because the animals were also entitled to a restful Sunday. For the theme *Sunday* cf. also Jeremias Gotthelf, *Zeitgeist und Bernergeist*, chap. 1, "Of a Sunday," which begins: "There probably isn't any word with a more beautiful sound to the ears of the real people in all countries than the word Sunday." Bonhoeffer had just read this book in May 1943; see *LPP*, pp. 40, 125.

4. Deleted: this most precious gift of Christianity

5. Deleted: this precious and kind commandment of God

6. Deleted: the warbling and call notes of the thrushes

7. Deleted: of the ravenous [?] young in their nests deep in the bushes

8. An editor of Latin school texts.

9. For the criticism of the sermon, cf. *Finkenwalder Homiletik, GS* 4, pp. 237ff., esp. p. 252; Eng. trans. "Bonhoeffer's Lectures on Preaching," in Clyde E. Fant, *Bonhoeffer: Worldly Preaching* (Nashville and New York: Thomas Nelson, 1975), pp. 123ff. The sympathy for the youthful members of the family who mostly didn't go to church on Sundays at the Bonhoeffers' is also characteristic here.

10. Here follows a deleted section: The minister had preached about the story of plucking the corn on the Sabbath Day and about the words of the Lord: "The Son of man is Lord even of the Sabbath Day." Why had he not said that Jesus had broken the law of the Sabbath in holy willfulness, not from need—for the disciples would not have starved if they had waited a few hours longer to eat—nor to do good? No, Jesus had simply acted and spoken with the authority of the One standing above any law—he, the Son of God, the Free One, the Lord. But what he was allowed to do and with him the very few following him, the rest of us aren't allowed to do by a long shot. It is for us first to take seriously and learn again to keep the Sabbath before we are permitted to recognize its ultimate keeping in the breaking of the law. After all, it was none other but the Son of God, and he alone, who profaned the Sabbath. Instead, the preacher this morning couldn't think of anything better to say than that there is no difference between a working day and a holiday for a Christian, and that Christian freedom consists in everybody spending the holiday as he thinks best. One can find God outside in the fields as well as in church.

11. Even in Bonhoeffer's childhood, his own family had had such an experience on an occasional visit to the church in Grunewald, and it later corresponded fairly closely to Frau von Kleist-Retzow's situation in the parish of Gross-Tychow, to which Kieckow and Klein-Krössin belonged. Therefore the von Kleists tried to have the pastors of the Confessing Church conduct regular services in their own chapel in Kieckow.

12. Deleted: Under no circumstances did she want to act from personal motives.

13. Echoes of the analysis in "Inheritance and Decay," *E*, pp. 88ff., esp. pp. 97ff. and 108–9.

14. Deleted: was deep in thought

15. According to German custom the women address each other by their husbands' titles, so Frau Brake is addressed in the original as "Frau Mayor," Frau Warmblut as "Frau Director."

16. Deleted: I'll tell you the connection.

17. Matt. 12:8.

18. 1 Sam. 16:7.

19. Deleted: Frau Karoline Brake walked through the spacious hall into the living room and from there onto the veranda where she sat down on a cane chair facing the garden

20. The clothes hooks did in fact exist for the eight brothers and sisters in the big house on Wangenheimstrasse in Berlin-Grunewald.

21. Dietrich had to get his father a Spanish shawl in Barcelona as a birthday present for his mother. The stick with the silver knob existed too.

22. Feuerbach played a decisive though mainly theological role for Dietrich Bonhoeffer himself; see *GS 5*, pp. 186, 193, 323; see also *LPP*, p. 360.

23. The oldest brother, and later physicist, Karl-Friedrich, returned from World War I with leftist convictions, and there were difficulties, for instance, with the family of Karl Bonhoeffer's brother who was working for industry. Karl-Friedrich, and also Klaus, refused to join the father's fraternity, the Igel in Tübingen; Dietrich joined a few years later. The family cannot remember in this form the incident while making music on a Saturday, but they do remember a dispute with Karl-Friedrich when he once refused to participate in the celebration of Advent which was customary in the family circle. They regularly made music on Saturday evenings in the way described. Karl-Friedrich, incidentally, was a lifelong friend of Professor Robert Havemann, who now lives in East Berlin.

24. Deleted: voiced a contradiction

25. Deleted: in no way crazy but unobtrusive, simple, appropriate

26. Deleted: —one should never inquire [?] why—

27. Deleted: Since then it was definitely established for the children, and it was like a piece of their patrician pride that they did not go along with such extravaganzas

28. Concerning his having been brought up to value simplicity, quality, and matter-of-factness, especially by his father, see *inter alia, LPP*, pp. 386–87 and 273–74.

29. The source here is probably the theologian Karl August von Hase, his great-grandfather, highly respected by family and the public, along with Bonhoeffer's interest in the Lutheran confessors and protesters Paul Gerhardt and August F. C. Vilmar.

30. Deleted: of the great-great-grandfather had assumed for them that of a saint almost

31. In fact, the family paid little attention to the family club existing on the mother's side; see, *inter alia*, the book by Dr. Karl Alfred von Hase, *Unsere Hauschronik: Geschichte der Familie Hase in vier Jahrhunderten* (Breitkopf & Härtel, 1898).

32. Deleted: actually it doesn't occur to anyone to do something nice for him for a change

33. This corresponded to the situation at his parents' home.

34. Deleted: A warm smile passed across the grandmother's face when she thought of her grandchildren's love and respect for her son and daughter-in-law.

35. Here in place of the following story was first written only this later-deleted sentence: Eight-year-old Little Brother could find things to do on his own in the garden for hours at a time.

36. Deleted: made of newspaper

37. Deleted: But sometimes when my mother eats none of the meat and gives it all to the others, then I think we don't have enough and we are poor after all."

38. Deleted: Does your mother say so?" "No, my mother has never said so but other people say so sometimes

39. Deleted: Eight-year-old Little Brother could find things to do on his own in the garden for hours at a time.

40. Concerning the animal's death, see also the drama fragment, n. 6, pp. 175–76 above.

41. Here instead of the following conversation the sentences, then deleted: It was half an hour to Sunday dinner. During that time, a conversation began between grandson and grandmother which we will relate a little later.

42. Matt. 10:29.

43. Deleted: does he take it to him in heaven?"

44. Luke 12:6. Deleted: "So is the bird now with God in heaven?"

45. Deleted: "Why do they have to die then?"

46. Deleted: Also toward [illegible]?" "Yes, especially toward them."

47. The forest lake near Friedrichsbrunn ("Bergrat Müller's pond"), and the expert mushroom hunting which had come down to them from the grandfather Friedrich Bonhoeffer, were part of Bonhoeffer's youthful memories.

48. Cf. the Introduction, p. 5 above.

49. Deleted: a dance on a volcano

50. Deleted: content

51. Deleted: very deep in conversation

52. Deleted: who was very different from his older brother and

53. Deleted: which want to be formed in one's youth and in later years

still . . . [illegible]

54. Deleted: Beer for our gentlemen fellow students, nearly all in long pants of course—even before noon in

55. Deleted: and the whole a foretaste of academic freedom

56. The Bonhoeffer children didn't necessarily join class trips and school events; if they didn't seem worthwhile, one got an excuse.

57. Eberhard Bethge told Bonhoeffer once that his mother, a minister's widow, had worried that her son's acquaintance might lead him to adopt an inappropriate life style. His grandfather had been a village organist.

58. Deleted: that the poor devil

59. Marginal note: State, upper class, piety. Deleted: What you are saying, Christoph, I probably feel even more strongly than you do because I see it daily from both sides, yours and mine.

60. Deleted: cleverness

61. For the idea of a new upper class cf. the baptismal letter, *LPP*, p. 299, and also the drama fragment, pp. 33–34 above.

62. Deleted: of false ambition

63. Deleted: But he always spoke with peculiar warmth and from personal experience and . . . [illegible] and through the great modesty

64. Deleted: This time Ulrich had

65. Deleted: said much less in such conversations that Christoph and also upon others

66. Cf. *LPP*, pp. 386, 387–90; also *LPP*, pp. 129–30, 144–45, 161–62, and *passim*.

67. Cf. the passages about "unconscious Christianity" in the letters of July and August 1944, *LPP*, pp. 373, 380, 394. According to the passage here, Bonhoeffer deals with this idea already in the autumn of 1943. The first page of the manuscript is again written on yellow paper; see the Introduction, pp. 10–11 above.

68. Deleted: know about Christianity, there is

69. Gal. 3:28.

70. 1 Cor. 1:27–28.

71. The story of "Yellow Boots" is based on a dispute in the woods near the Silesian summer house at Wölfelsgrund in the first decade of this century between mother Bonhoeffer and the assistant forester who tried to intimidate and drive away the children.

72. Deleted: or I'll send you

73. Erroneously: Christoph.

74. Deleted: rabble

75. Deleted: and you'll get to feel one day

76. Deleted: pityingly

77. Deleted: I didn't mean it that way

78. Here and on the following pages Bonhoeffer first wrote "colonel,"

but then corrected everywhere to "general"; later, without correcting, he used the rank "major" and stuck to it. So we are using "major" throughout without further notes.

79. Deleted: Believe me, you'll smooth over your rough edges yet. Beware of yourself lest you make others unhappy.

80. Klara has many traits of Dietrich Bonhoeffer's eldest sister, Ursula (later Frau Schleicher).

81. Deleted: Well, didn't your father tell you that I live here? I have been wanting to visit you for a long time and tell him that I only

82. Bonhoeffer wrote "Anna" here but then "Sophie" to the end, therefore we use this name here from the beginning.

83. Deleted: asked

84. Deleted: to the castle

85. Deleted: and it seemed as though Franz were close to tears.

86. Deleted: with the workers' children in the East of the town

87. The Bonhoeffer family had had a long relationship with Friedrich Siegmund-Schultze who had built up a kind of settlement in the East of Berlin and initiated social work and social education. Through that, professional contacts with Karl Bonhoeffer's neurological clinic in the Charité were made. In 1922, Ursula and Klaus attended his lectures in Anna von Gierke's social-pedagogical seminar and the work in aid of prisoners (see the German edition of the biography, p. 68). Fraternity friends from the "Igel" worked as volunteers in Siegmund-Schultze's social work community on Fruchtstrasse. After 1926, Siegmund-Schultze was an honorary professor at Berlin's Faculty of Theology. Bonhoeffer's closest friend at that time, Franz Hildebrandt, was a curate with him in the east of Berlin. But one should also remember Bonhoeffer's own work at the Zionskirche with confirmation candidates from proletarian families and his wish to take on a pastorate in the east of Berlin (*DB*, pp. 168ff. and 172–73).

88. Deleted: and yet, under all brutality and filth I have

89. For the abuse of power and the "little tyrants" see the story from prison, "Lance Corporal Berg" in *LPP* pp. 253ff. and the section "Of Folly" in "After Ten Years," *LPP* p. 8–9.

90. Deleted: where he meets greater power

91. The following section deleted: Franz, the struggle of my life, and not only of *my* life, has been directed against these petty tyrants. But remember, they are not only more dangerous, but also stronger, tougher, harder to get hold of, than the big ones. They slip through your fingers when you want to grab them, for they are smooth and cowardly. But whoever succeeds in toppling one of them may boast of having saved many human lives; he becomes a benefactor of mankind even if no one is aware of it. Today like-minded people of our class have acquired the habit of smiling about these petty tyrants; they can afford it for they need not

fear them. But smiling about them is as foolish as smiling about the tiny size of bacteria and in reality it is a cowardly capitulation before the greater power of the countless petty people.

92. Deleted: Then he began himself. "You are sufficiently grown up to hear what I am now going to tell you. My oldest son Harald became the victim of such a petty tyrant two years ago. He was nineteen years old. I lost my oldest son Harald in this struggle." Cf. note 191 below.

93. Deleted: It is the last notes of his diary

94. Deleted: With that, the major turned to Ulrich and

95. Deleted: A strange feeling of embarrassment. . . . Come Christoph, what are you waiting for?

96. There had been family ties to South Africa only since 1933 when a second cousin, Hans-Jürgen von Hase, emigrated to the then German South West Africa, though there was hardly any close contact with him. The emigration of Tafel ancestors to the United States during the 1840's was always consciously remembered; Dietrich Bonhoeffer possessed writings by Swedenborg from his emigré great-great-uncle, and also visited his descendants in Philadelphia in 1930 and 1939. In view of the situation of the Blacks, Bonhoeffer had of course known since his visits to Harlem in 1930 and his trip to the United States in 1939 why Renate said "impossible things" (p. 90 above). (When his characters speak of "Negroes" Bonhoeffer of course reflects the usage that was universal until the late 1960s when the Black Power movement in the United States, with its slogan "black is beautiful," raised consciousness about, and overcame, the racism in such usage.) The problem of being part of two countries and two cultures had faced him daily during his 1933–35 London pastorate, and was grievously close in the fate of his twin sister's family, exiled in 1938.

97. Deleted: "Well, half and half," says Renate. "You know that my mother is English. My homeland is where my parents are."

98. Deleted: this estate has belonged to my father's family for many centuries

99. Deleted: I think it's great

100. Deleted: then I was happy

101. The following first version was deleted: —such a peaceful and quiet [and again deleted: quiet, industrious, loyal] Negro on our plantations, I simply like him better than our arrogant, presumptuous, and grouchy inspector or steward or mayor or policeman [deleted: as I see them here so often]."

"But these Negroes are slaves, so to speak, Renate," Christoph objected somewhat disapprovingly.

Slaves? Nonsense; at any rate everything there is much more human and personal than it is here where everybody wants some official status if possible and prides himself on it. It really is like that, Christoph; I sometimes long for an evening on the farm when the Negroes sit in front of their huts and sing—they sing beautifully and have beautiful songs—and greet you peaceably when you ride by. No, they are not slaves, they have their pride, too. But they have it in a different way.

102. Deleted: I think it's so difficult here

103. The following section is heavily self-analytical in view of his personal experiences of dominance, of having been brought up to deal with inner difficulties by himself, of his experiences of *"tristitia"* (*LPP*, p. 129) and the breakthrough to oral confession; see also passages about the impossibility of direct access to one another in *Life Together*, in the Finkenwalde Seelsorge (*GS* 5, pp. 363ff.), and also about "covering up" (*LPP*, pp. 158-59).

104. Deleted: and wherever Christoph saw an obligation come his way. . . . Christoph was one of the people who . . . he saw an obligation come his way . . . and wherever he recognized obligations there was

105. Deleted: he had once said to Ulrich: "There must be meaning in the fact that God already . . . by nature"

106. Deleted: which he knew how to tackle

107. In his literary estate there are numerous picture postcards, for example, of gates and churches in towns in Mecklenburg, as souvenirs of trips Bonhoeffer took in the early twenties with brothers and sisters, his cousin Hans Christoph von Hase, and fellow students; in addition, a series of letters to his parents also happens to include the description of a night trip to Sylt with fishermen (*GS* 6, pp. 94ff.).

108. Deleted: come along on such a trip

109. Deleted: behind the glittering or brittle facade

110. Deleted: But he himself, Christoph, was to be the mediator for all this; he had to give himself an account now of what Germany actually was.

111. Deleted: Renate didn't put a single question to Christoph

112. The following first draft deleted: What he didn't say she didn't want to ask about. How could she penetrate into the sphere of his life? [Deleted: Personal words are free words of one to the other. Such words that come out of one's own life are free gifts. She wanted the pure gift which in a life. . . .] Words that come out of one's personal life are free gifts to be received as such. [Forced] The least trace of inner compulsion makes them worthless. Out of the freely flowing word of the one, the magic wand is . . . springs the word of the other who opens up the pure source [deleted: of the other's word] of the word in the other. [Deleted: thus every word was a free gift of the one to the other.]

113. The following draft deleted: [Deleted: Slowly and conversing comfortably the last group was seen] Frau von Bremer and Klara had taken their time and in the distance one could see the two tall women approach slowly, conversing comfortably. Next to the blonde woman with the large,

expressive, blue eyes, young Klara walked in her light-colored linen dress, embroidered by herself, over which hung low the heavy, dark braids. Despite all their differences, the same free, composed, confident walk of the two women revealed something related, a shared basis of life; only women from old families walk like that, women who have always known themselves safe under the protection of their brothers and husbands and in the strong realm of their families; but they still walk like that when they meet up with disaster, and the protection they have lost surrounds each of their steps like an invisible force which no one dares approach.

114. Deleted: beside the figure who with her approximately forty years still appeared youthful

115. Deleted: Young Klara had had to tell the new aunt also about the life of the family

116. The following first version deleted: . . . that she had taken on since finishing school the previous Easter. Every word was spoken with such warmth and simplicity that Frau von Bremer took a strong liking to Klara. She had not met many young German girls so far; neither the pleasure-seeking and inwardly uncommitted daughters of rich merchants that she had seen abroad and in Germany, nor the emancipated students, nor yet the unfree, anxious, semi-cultured so-called high society girls had impressed her; she wished to think of none of them as a companion for Renate. [Deleted: But here she met for the first time]

117. Deleted: as she had learned from her grandmother

118. Deleted: interrupted only by her concern that Grandmother had everything she needed. . . . Small ministrations with which she attentively took care of her grandmother

119. Deleted: see in a new light

120. Deleted: she learned to enjoy the variety of the world in small things

121. Deleted: that everywhere light and shadow are together and that a kind and humble heart is the greatest human blessing

122. The description of music-making preferences and attending Bach's *Passions* and *Mass in B Minor* was valid for the whole family. To study *Art of Fugue,* Bonhoeffer and Bethge bought and played an arrangement for two pianos (see *LPP*, p. 219).

123. Deleted: It was hard for the mother

124. How strongly Bonhoeffer himself suffered from homesickness (for example, in the United States in June, 1939, and even more in Tegel) he made very clear in his letters, and also how he dealt with it: see *LPP* pp. 167ff. and 183ff., and also the passages about dealing with longing, *LPP,* pp. 176ff. and 271ff.

125. Deleted: Klara was very surprised. She hadn't spent a single day of her life away from her parents or brothers.

126. Deleted: helps her mother from morning till night

127. The following first version deleted: would frankly not like to be separated from them." Frau von Bremer was wise enough not to be the least bit offended by this frank refusal. On the contrary, she almost liked Klara even better for this attachment to her family. She was a girl who wasn't always after something new, hungering for experience, but who preferred the constant, tried, and true. This girl would only have shaken her head smiling in amazement at the motto: "Live intensely," which meant: "always seek new strong impressions, throw yourself into the vortex of life, learn to love and discard men, don't allow anything to bind and fetter you, enjoy everything to the full and, above all, be independent." Klara didn't need any of this, she lived more intensely than most. She would have thought, or at any rate felt, that not change but constancy could make a woman's life fulfilled.

"It is good," Frau von Bremer thought, "that she didn't accept right away. She is hard to win over but when she is won she holds fast. [Deleted: She kept on thinking, it is good too when a girl doesn't let herself be invited so easily. Anyway, there is a big difference between children who enjoy being invited and those who don't.] Klara probably was one of those people—like herself—who like to invite but dislike being invited. With adults that is easily a sign of superiority, indolence, and coldness, with children

128. The twin sister Sabine Leibholz tells that when she came home one day from her drawing class and reported that the teacher had told her: "Fräulein Bonhoeffer, you must live more intensely," it had become a household word; however, from then on they didn't consider this art school suitable, and she didn't go there anymore.

129. Deleted: Delighted with these ideas and full of plans for tomorrow, Frau von Bremer and Klara met the others who were somewhat impatiently waiting at the spit

130. Deleted: "It is our only luxury!" said the major, "whoever gets used to it once

131. Deleted: to visit the house and the stables

132. Deleted: and they had only heard from the grandmother.
(Even in his memoirs [see drama fragment, note 6, above], Karl Bonhoeffer gave only scanty information.)

133. Deleted: I considered it a certainty that there too I would soon assume the leadership again, and was looking forward to

134. Deleted: that I couldn't imagine at all

135. Deleted: last

136. Deleted: Here is only one will, that of the whole class. Here is your seat." Or perhaps your own, I would have liked to shout.

137. Deleted: the greatest fellow in the whole school but one must obey

138. Obviously these are personal experiences in the high school in

Berlin-Grunewald with Director Vilmar, especially classes with the eminent Hellenist Dr. Walther Kranz for whom Dietrich wrote his elective thesis "Catullus and Horace as Lyric Poets" (see the German edition of the biography, pp. 68ff.).

139. Deleted: didn't disdain courting his favor. I must repeat, the astonishing thing in all that was that

140. Deleted: and it was something mysterious . . . but he had a mysterious influence on anyone meeting him

141. Deleted: and no one seemed to pay any attention to me

142. Deleted: He was only two years older than I

143. Deleted: We'll talk about it later

144. Deleted: "You'll understand later."

145. In the first German edition of this book we reported that biographical models for this story of rivalry and friendship between the two students were not known to the editors, either from Dietrich Bonhoeffer's life or from his father's. After it was published we received a communication from Hans Krause, now an engineer in Jerusalem. Krause and Dietrich Bonhoeffer were classmates at the Friedrich Werder Gymnasium in Berlin, where Bonhoeffer was a pupil from Autumn, 1913 to Spring, 1919. Krause reports that this rivalry story reminded him of an incident between Dietrich Bonhoeffer and his fellow pupil Ernst Abrahamson; the latter later became a professor of classics and comparative literature in the United States where he died in 1958. At first Dietrich Bonhoeffer was the obvious leader of the class, and the extraordinarily gifted Abrahamson was his rival. Then a sort of conspiracy arose. One day a group of Abrahamson's friends fell upon Dietrich Bonhoeffer in order to thrash him, making a certain K.B. (a fellow pupil from a proletarian family) a prominent participant. Later Dietrich Bonhoeffer and Ernst Abrahamson became friends, and Bonhoeffer's dominance came to an end. In a class photo taken about 1917, Dietrich and Ernst sit side by side among the thirty-four pupils (including Hans Krause). Incidentally, in Karl Bonhoeffer's family book (he made entries each New Year), the entry for 1915 under Dietrich includes this comment: "He fights a lot and enjoys it."

146. Deleted: [illegible] Hans, too, who for a long time had acted with unfailing kindness towards me, though we never exchanged more than a few words, began to look at me with distrust and unfriendliness.

147. Deleted: will with no one . . . I don't appreciate

148. Deleted: to trap me somehow and make me do something stupid that would . . . me from school

149. Addition in the margin: In his attitude towards me I felt at the same time a certain sadness and a certain warmth.

150. Deleted: or at least to share it with Hans

151. Deleted: tore it from my hand with an indescribable expression
152. Deleted: That was the end, I sensed it
153. The following first version deleted:

"What do you mean by that, Uncle Harald?" Christoph asked after a while.

"Well, that is hard to say in a word," he answered. "You see, there are people who always want to accomplish everything alone and believe they have to succeed in everything and that everyone else must submit to their will. When two such people meet, they chafe against each other and cannot get along even though they really have nothing against each other and though each basically respects the other. But each simply cannot stand to have the other as an equal. Then a lot of wrong happens; there are opposing parties, enmity, battles, intrigue, and all for no good reason, only because nobody wants to have his power curtailed. So it was with Hans and me, perhaps without either of us really knowing it.

154. Deleted: This dream blinded Hans against his classmates and against me, and it prevented me from rightly acknowledging Hans as my superior.

155. The following versions deleted: and 'All or nothing.' That sounds very nice and maybe prophets can live according to such a motto. But for the daily life of people together—let me tell you! It's a terrible disaster. To crush someone else, figuratively and literally, doesn't need any character. Any yielding shows a lack of character!! Turn enemies into friends!

That sounds very impressive but—it is sophomoric. Men think like that who have no good judgment in human relationships, no contact yet with real life, and no sense of existing people. One can't expect much more from sophomores, but with adults it is a disaster. To crush someone else, figuratively or in reality, only because he is different from me, doesn't need any character.

156. Bonhoeffer had already treated the ethical-theological background of radicalism and compromise in the winter of 1940–41 in the section "The Last Things and the Things before the Last" in his *Ethics; E*, pp. 120ff. See also the sections about "Correspondence with Reality," *E*, pp. 227–35, and "The World of Things—Pertinence—Statecraft," *E*, pp. 235–40. These sections come under the heading "The Structure of Responsible Life," *E*, pp. 224ff., which also deals with the problem of the use of power and force by a Christian.

157. Deleted: it will also appear that such dreamers always find followers who confirm them in their dreams; that's how it was with me before school, in school with Hans

158. Deleted: nothing at all

159. Deleted: Georg had long been waiting for an opportune moment to get a word in. When his father stopped now, the boy burst out with

the question: "Father, may Martin and I leave the table?" That came as such a surprise that there was loud laughter all around which Georg didn't understand at all.

160. The following first version deleted: Now Franz joined the conversation; what Uncle had said made him think of his history teacher in school, a highly intelligent and cultured man; however, he had [deleted: often been angry with him] never been able to agree with him; for whether he presented the French Revolution or the Reformation or the origins of Christianity, the result was always—and this he stated to the class with an [deleted: somewhat superior] ambiguous smile and as if with some sarcasm—that all that remained of the great ideas and movements was only a mediocre compromise. That was the lesson of history and life that we should remember. I once clashed with him strongly because I told him that what he called the results of history one could just as well consider its dissolution and fall. I [deleted: wasn't at all interested] didn't want to sniff around in history's smell of decay all the time, but for my part would stick to its high points. Those were the results and lessons of history for me.

"You are a pretty good dialectician," the major said smiling, "and what did the history teacher answer?"

He said he didn't insist on specific words; everyone should stick to what was important to him; only I shouldn't tell him anything about the so-called high points. In retrospect they looked pretty good, but that was a great deception, and nothing was more dangerous than for the historians to paint these times as shining models which people should strive to imitate. For all those who had had to personally experience these so-called times, they had been the most horrible times in the whole history of the world, and he regarded it as fortunate that such a time happened only every few hundred years and made a generation of people unhappy. During the great times man and his life and happiness counted for nothing at all; it was the [illegible] who thirst for the blood of human sacrifices just to erect an altar to some sort of idea. Apart from that, I should look at the heroes of the great times—Jesus, Luther, Cromwell, Robespierre—and consider whether one of them had been happy or had even wanted only happiness for man. At the end, they had all basically cried like Jesus: "My God, why hast thou forsaken me?" When I asked at last whether man had been created to be unhappy he looked at me sideways, with an expression I couldn't interpret but which was not unkind, and said such problems weren't in his domain and unfortunately he didn't know in whose they were; but he was ready to discuss this question with me again twenty years from now. Even as a small boy I always got annoyed by such postponements and saw them as nothing but an evasion of the answer."

"Sometimes it is indeed the only possible answer, Franz," the major said calmly, "but of course only sometimes."

161. Actually, only Dr. Kranz mentioned above was really respected by the Bonhoeffer children.

162. Deleted: were the greatest moments of my years in school

163. Deleted: from this disruption . . . was suffering

164. For the judgments about the French Revolution and the Reformation, see the section "Inheritance and Decay" from the autumn of 1940, *E*, pp. 88ff.

165. Gen. 6:4.

166. Deleted: through great difficulties the real

167. Deleted: what we have both renounced, namely

168. Cf. Bonhoeffer's idea of relational freedom, developed early: "Only in relationship with the other am I free. No . . . individualistic concept of freedom can conceive of freedom," *CF*, p. 37; that was in 1932. See also the letter from Geneva to London in September, 1941, where the discussion of the history of freedoms ends with: "In the first place, freedom is not an *individual* right but a *responsibility*. In the first place, freedom is not focused on the individual but on the neighbor" (*GS* 1, 359–60). In addition, the concept of reality in the *Ethics* sees the love of Christ neither positivistically nor normatively but as the love of real life.

169. Klaus Bonhoeffer used the idea of wasteful nature frequently, especially movingly in his farewell letter to his parents from the Lehrterstrasse Prison (*Auf dem Wege zur Freiheit* [Berlin: 1946], p. 40).

170. Deleted: with every word

171. The following first version deleted: you propose as the ultimate lesson of history and life. But doesn't everything rather depend on what kind of life we love and with whom we are to live and get along? Shall we give up all of that just to live with one another and get along together? Only the substance of life is decisive. You condemn 'all or nothing'? Doesn't every religion and ethic make this claim, and mustn't its disciples act accordingly? Doesn't he who fails to do so become a traitor to himself? Isn't the true and the good more important than peace? Isn't there far too much indolent peace among men, and don't we have to scare them out of it? Don't people need firm principles today by which they must live and for which they must die? And precisely because most people are indolent and cowardly—mustn't there be masters and servants, yes I might almost say: Slaves? Wasn't Aristotle right when he taught that there are people born slaves by nature, and wasn't Schiller wrong with his revolutionary slogan, " 'man is born free, is free . . .'? But for those, the few really free people, the elite, the leaders, love of life and happiness cannot be the ultimate norm. Isn't an unhappy human being more than a happy pet? I have just read the story of Don Quixote and Sancho Panza."

172. Bonhoeffer had bought the complete edition of Cervantes's *Don Quixote* during his pastorate in Barcelona in 1928–29 and read it then in

the original language. The theme caught his interest anew while he was working on *Ethics* and he commented on "an old world [which] ventures to take up arms against a new one. It is all too easy to pour scorn on the weapons which we have inherited from our fathers, the weapons which served them to perform great feats but which in the present struggle can no longer be sufficient" (*E*, p. 67–68, in the autumn of 1940); and in 1941 he wrote: "Good is not in itself an independent theme for life; if it were so it would be the craziest kind of quixotry" (*E*, p. 191).

173. Deleted: equality

174. Deleted: Certainly, there will be greater tasks for you than for us and you must be sober and tough to master them.

175. Deleted: talking, and making heroes of unhappy human beings

176. Deleted: immoderate barbaric

177. Deleted: Let me say it very bluntly and distinctly for once, I consider it a sin to flirt with unhappiness.

178. Deleted: It seems to me that this philosophy stems from a dubious surfeit of happiness

179. Deleted: It is playing with fire. It is a more dangerous illusion than everything else.

180. See the poem "Sorrow and Joy" of June, 1944, *LPP*, pp. 334–35.

181. Deleted: He read in her . . . Immediately he recalled the conversation he had had with her just an hour ago

182. Deleted: tacitly asked him to help her love Germany, after all

183. Cf. note 3 above.

184. The motif of the bells is also in Jeremias Gotthelf; see note 3 above.

185. The following draft deleted: The old minister said that Misericordia had been cast in the first years of the Reformation and was donated to the church by an ancestor of your father. For almost four hundred years the people of this area have heard these bells, and ancestors and forefathers have been awakened and buried during their tolling. The people here call the tolling of all three bells on Sunday evenings the 'great evening blessing.' On weekdays, when only Justitia is rung, they call that the 'little evening blessing.' Bells are the good spirit of a country. As long as they ring, a country cannot get completely lost, I think. Come, let us briefly

186. Deleted: might have lived at the beginning of the triple peal

187. That's how the view still was in Dietrich Bonhoeffer's youth; it could be seen from the edge of the village of Friedrichsbrunn where the summer house was.

188. Deleted: the yellow, white, and blue wildflowers with especially

189. Wisd. of Sol. 3:1.

190. Deleted: and finally because I wish that you and my children will become acquainted and be close to each other

191. See the drama fragment, note 6, with reference to the suicide of

the cousin Wolf, Count von Kalckreuth; see also the detailed reports about him in his brother's book: Johannes Kalckreuth, *Wesen und Werk meines Vaters. Lebensbild des Malers Graf Leopold von Kalckreuth* (Hamburg: 1967), especially pp. 311–320 about the suicide of the nineteen-year-old in Cannstatt on October 9, 1906, about his connection with Rilke, and about his early literary efforts. Unfortunately there is no clue about the kind of circumstances Bonhoeffer had in mind for the death of this son of the von Bremers. Perhaps the atmosphere of this scene also contains elements of the parents' and children's experiences in 1918 when Walter was killed; cf. especially the description by Sabine Leibholz-Bonhoeffer, *The Bonhoeffers: Portrait of a Family* (London: Sidgwick & Jackson; New York: St. Martin's Press, 1972), pp. 21–24.

192. Deleted: But, thank God, we were not broken by it

193. Deleted: who caused us such great sorrow

DOCUMENTS

1. Julie Bonhoeffer, née Tafel, Dietrich Bonhoeffer's grandmother (the personal peerage had been bestowed upon her husband; she didn't make use of it, however).

2. On Fräulein Horn see *DB* pp. 13, 21; Sabine Leibholz, née Bonhoeffer; Elisabeth von Hase, the mother's sister, living in Breslau; Prof. Czerny, a pediatrician at the Charité; Dr. Czeppan was a curiosity among the acquaintances of the family as a "Deutschnationaler" (this party first voted for Hindenburg and then in 1931 joined with Hitler's NSDAP in the "Harzburger Front").

3. The meaning is that none of the brothers and sisters was thirty yet in 1926.

4. Stuttgart: the young couple Rüdiger Schleicher and Ursula, née Bonhoeffer; Hamburg: the young couple Hans von Dohnanyi and Christine, née Bonhoeffer.

5. Miericke's was a coffeehouse in Grunewald around the corner from the Bonhoeffer house; A. Wertheim was the Macy's or Selfridges of Berlin in those days.

6. Move from 14 Wangenheimstrasse to 43 Marienburgerallee.

7. Karl Bonhoeffer, Professor of Neurology and Psychiatry, 1868–1948; Hans Delbrück, Professor of History, 1848–1929.

8. Hans von Dohnanyi, Christine von Dohnanyi, née Bonhoeffer; Justus Delbrück; Grete Bonhoeffer, née von Dohnanyi (Karl-Friedrich's wife); Sabine Leibholz, née Bonhoeffer; Klaus Bonhoeffer; Emmi Bonhoeffer, née Delbrück; Susanne Dress, née Bonhoeffer; Max Delbrück, Dietrich Bonhoeffer; Karl-Friedrich Bonhoeffer; Gerhard Leibholz.

DIETRICH BONHOEFFER'S PRISON FICTION:
A COMMENTARY

1. *LPP*, pp. 253–60.
2. *DB*, p. 12.
3. *LPP*, pp. 294ff.
4. Theodore A. Gill, discussion following the presentation of his paper "Bonhoeffer as Aesthete," on November 1, 1975, at the Annual Meeting of the American Academy of Religion, in Chicago, Illinois.
5. *DB*, pp. 528–30.
6. Hans Mommsen, "Social Views and Constitutional Plans of the Resistance" in Hermann Graml, Hans Mommsen, Hans-Joachim Reichhardt, and Ernst Wolf, *The German Resistance to Hitler* (Berkeley and Los Angeles: University of California Press, 1970), p. 64.
7. Ibid., pp. 64–65.
8. Ibid., pp. 98ff.
9. *LPP*, p. 17.
10. Walter Struve, *Elites Against Democracy: Leadership Ideals in Bourgeois Political Thought in Germany, 1890–1933* (Princeton: Princeton University Press, 1973), p. 3.
11. Mommsen, "Social Views," p. 72.
12. *LPP*, p. 3.
13. See Elisabeth Kübler-Ross, *On Death and Dying* (New York: The Macmillan Company, 1969), and Raymond A. Moody, Jr., *Life after Life* (Atlanta: Mockingbird Books, 1975).
14. *DB*, p. 736.
15. *LPP*, pp. 163, 271. After nine months in prison Bonhoeffer concluded: "It's possible to get used to physical hardships, and to live for months out of the body, so to speak—almost too much so—but one doesn't get used to the psychological strain; on the contrary, I have the feeling that everything that I see and hear is putting years on me, and I'm often finding the world nauseating and burdensome." *LPP*, p. 162.
16. Carl Friedrich von Weizsäcker, "Thoughts of a Non-Theologian on Dietrich Bonhoeffer's Theological Development," *The Ecumenical Review* (XXVIII. 2, April 1976), p. 169.
17. *LPP*, p. 129.
18. Ernst Kris, *Psychoanalytic Explorations in Art* (New York: International Universities Press, 1952), pp. 291–302 ("On Inspiration"). On p. 251 Kris refers to John Dewey's "convincing" argument that aesthetic creation may be looked on as a type of problem-solving behavior. See John Dewey, *Art as Experience* (New York: Minton, Balch, and Company, 1934), especially pp. 15–16.

19. *LPP*, p. 70.

20. Dietrich Bonhoeffer, *Widerstand und Ergebung: Briefe und Auf-
zeichnungen aus der Haft, Neuausgabe*, edited by Eberhard Bethge (Munich:
Christian Kaiser Verlag, 1970), p. 296. The English translation of "Hohe
Spannungen geben starke Funken" is mine and slightly different from the
translation in *LPP*, p. 272. Dietrich Bonhoeffer also used this phrase in
conversations with a fellow prisoner, Gaetano Latmiral. (Interview with
Professor Gaetano Latmiral in Geneva, Switzerland, February 5, 1976.)

21. *LPP*, p. 319.

22. ". . . Everything that has happened in the last seven and a half
months has left both of us essentially unchanged; I never doubted it for
a moment, and you certainly didn't either." *LPP*, p. 145. Heartened by
a rare opportunity to see Eberhard Bethge in a prison visit, Bonhoeffer
exclaimed: "I never doubted that you would come back the same person
who went and that we would understand each other in everything without
any change." *LPP*, pp. 301ff. "In short, it was very splendid for both of
us to be together and I can't imagine that anything will change in the years
to come." *LPP*, p. 329.

23. *LPP*, pp. 131, 308.
24. *LPP*, pp. 207–208.
25. *LPP*, p. 160.
26. *LPP*, p. 277.
27. *LPP*, p. 162.
28. *LPP*, pp. 71, 164.
29. *LPP*, p. 217.
30. *LPP*, pp. 178, 272.
31. *LPP*, pp. 300, 344.
32. *LPP*, p. 135.
33. *LPP*, pp. 50; 263, note 53.
34. *LPP*, p. 114.
35. *LPP*, p. 71.
36. *LPP*, p. 303.
37. *LPP*, pp. 94, 312.
38. *LPP*, p. 94.
39. *LPP*, pp. 129–130.
40. Drama fragment, above, p. 34.
41. Drama fragment, above, pp. 18, 19, 22f.
42. Drama fragment, above, p. 46.
43. Novel fragment, above, p. 93.
44. Novel fragment, above, p. 117.
45. Novel fragment, above, p. 117.
46. *LPP*, p. 416. Bonhoeffer made this statement about *Life Together*

to his fiancée, Maria von Wedemeyer. See Dietrich Bonhoeffer, *Life Together*, translated by John W. Doberstein (New York: Harper and Brothers, Publishers, 1954).

47. Gerhard Jacobi, "Drawn Towards Suffering"; *IKDB*, p. 71.

48. Novel fragment, above, p. 93.

49. Novel fragment, p. 76.

50. Novel fragment, p. 51.

51. See Ruth Zerner, "Dietrich Bonhoeffer's American Experiences: People, Letters, and Papers from Union Seminary," *Union Seminary Quarterly Review*, (XXXI. 4, Summer 1976) especially pp. 266–273.

52. *LPP*, pp. 253–260.

53. Kris, *Psychoanalytic Explorations*, p. 253. The term "regression" has frequently been used by psychiatrists to refer to behavior patterns that denote maladjustment, disharmony, or peculiarity in return to earlier forms of behavior. More and more psychiatrists, however, have been using the word "regression" in new, varied, and sophisticated ways, indicating that the mechanism of regression does not always refer to pathologically negative behavior. Kris, for example, explores the creative dimensions of regression as part of the process of artistic production. Two other psychiatrists, Henry Krystal and T. A. Petty, studying rehabilitation from physical illness, conclude that "the restorative value of regression has not received attention commensurate with its importance." (H. Krystal, M.D., and T. A. Petty, M.D., "Rehabilitation in Trauma following Illness, Physical Injury, and Massive Personality Damage," in Henry Krystal, M.D., ed., *Massive Psychic Trauma* [New York: International Universities Press, 1968], p. 281.) In addition to the positive effects of psychiatrically designated "regression" in artistic creation and in physical recuperation from trauma, one of the most respected recent psychiatric publications on adolescence maintains that regression is a necessary component of the adolescent transition to adulthood. Written by the psychoanalyst Peter Blos, this work does not focus on malignant, psychotic regression, but rather on regression which leads to healthy growth and development. Peter Blos, *The Adolescent Passage: Developmental Issues* (New York: International Universities Press, 1979). Thus psychiatrists themselves have rescued the term "regression" from purely negative connotations concerning childish behavior. They have expanded its psychiatric meaning to include creative reflection on the past.

54. Norman H. Holland, *Psychoanalysis and Shakespeare* (New York: McGraw-Hill Book Company, 1964, 1966), p. 338.

55. *LPP*, p. 169.

56. *LPP*, p. 346.

57. Thomas I. Day, "Conviviality and Common Sense: The Meaning of Christian Community for Dietrich Bonhoeffer" (Ph.D. dissertation, New

York: Union Theological Seminary, 1975), p. 630. Stressing that "for his patriarchal community Bonhoeffer urged an ethics of 'noblesse oblige'," Day correctly points out that "Bonhoeffer was no democrat and saw authority inherent in service as descending from above rather than coming up from below." Ibid., pp. 527, 618.

58. Gal. 3:28. Novel fragment, above, p. 000.

59. Novel fragment, above, p. 000. Bonhoeffer later mentions the phrase in a letter to Bethge postmarked July 27, 1944, and in notes of July/August 1944, *LPP*, pp. 373, 380. Bethge refers to the importance of the phrase in a letter of August 24, 1944, *LPP*, p. 394. But there is no further development of this concept in the remaining letters.

60. *LPP*, pp. 281–282.

61. *LPP*, p. 345.

62. *LPP*, pp. 361, 369. Dietrich Bonhoeffer, *The Cost of Discipleship, Revised Edition* (New York: The Macmillan Company, 1963), pp. 47–49. For an analysis of Bonhoeffer's attitude toward Jews, see Ruth Zerner, "Dietrich Bonhoeffer and the Jews; Thoughts and Actions, 1933–1945," *Jewish Social Studies* (XXXVII. 3–4, Summer/Fall 1975), pp. 235–250. The importance of Christians' rediscovery of their "Jewishness" has been recognized by Eberhard Bethge, who has suggested that by studying New Testament sources with Jews, Christians may "become richer by winning back the Jewish context, especially the Jewish sense of history and exegesis." Eberhard Bethge, "The Holocaust and Christian Anti-Semitism: Perspectives of a Christian Survivor," *Union Seminary Quarterly Review* (XXXII. 3–4, Spring/Summer 1977), p. 154. See, above all, Eberhard Bethge, "Bonhoeffer and the Jews," in *Ethical Responsibility: Bonhoeffer's Legacy to the Churches*, ed. Geffrey B. Kelly and John D. Godsey (New York: Edwin Mellen Press, 1981), pp. 43–102.

63. *LPP*, p. 393.

64. *LPP*, pp. 370–372.

65. *LPP*, p. 309.

66. *LPP*, pp. 167–169.

67. *LPP*, p. 199.

68. Drama fragment, above, pp. 25–26.

69. *LPP*, p. 280.

70. *LPP*, p. 361.

71. *LPP*, p. 129.

72. *LPP*, p. 125. See Jeremias Gotthelf, *Zeitgeist und Berner Geist* (Erlenbach-Zürich: Eugen Reutsch Verlag, 1959, originally published in 1851), p. 11. The first paragraph of this Gotthelf novel, a favorite of Bonhoeffer's, projects several of the key images and ideas also found in Bonhoeffer's novel fragment "Sunday": a village church, bells, the significance of Sunday for harmony, rest, and re-creation of the spirit.

73. *LPP*, pp. 158, 162. Adalbert Stifter's last novel, *Witiko*, gave Bonhoeffer special pleasure in prison: "For me it's one of the finest books I know. The purity of its style and character drawing gives one a quite rare and peculiar feeling of happiness." *LPP*, p. 125. In Stifter's novel the ideals of pure, moral Teutonic knighthood are embodied in the medieval warrior, Witiko, who enters battle not for plunder or violence, but for defensive purposes ("defending father, mother, brothers, sisters, neighbors, and one's people"). Seized by a strong sense of honor, Witiko prepares for battle by focusing all of his energies on it, expecting the conflict to ennoble, not to degrade him. Adalbert Stifter, *Witiko* (Munich: Winkler Verlag, 1949, originally published in 1865-67), pp. 31-32.

One British scholar and student of Adalbert Stifter's works has seen in Stifter's *Witiko* (one of Bonhoeffer's favorite novels) characteristics which reflect the values, vision, and impact of Bonhoeffer's life: *Witiko* "is a triumphal asseveration of Stifter's faith in that forward march of humanity towards ordered, cultured living. . . . The vision is vast and sublime, the individual both insignificant and profoundly responsible. . . . The guiding rule of our lives must be: *'Tun, was die Dinge fordern'*, and then . . . we shall find our true inheritance, and rise to greatness, true greatness in the sphere of the *'sanftes Gesetz'*." Eric A. Blackall, *Adalbert Stifter: A Critical Study* (Cambridge: Cambridge University Press, 1948), pp. 389-390.

74. *LPP*, p. 372.

75. *LPP*, pp. 217-218.

76. *LPP*, p. 309.

77. *LPP*, p. 88.

78. *LPP*, p. 136.

79. See Hannah Arendt, *Eichmann in Jerusalem* (New York: Viking Press, 1963).

80. *LPP*, p. 218.

81. *LPP*, p. 314.

82. *LPP*, p. 17. In a 1942 letter to his twin sister, Sabine Leibholz, and her husband, Bonhoeffer also stressed the lessons of suffering: "So it is good to learn early enough that suffering and God is not a contradiction but rather a necessary unity; for me the idea that God himself is suffering has always been one of the most convincing teachings of Christianity. I think God is nearer to suffering than to happiness and to find God in this way gives peace and rest and a strong and courageous heart." (*GS*, 6, p. 557; English translation in Sabine Leibholz-Bonhoeffer, *The Bonhoeffers: Portrait of a Family* [London: Sidgwick & Jackson; New York: St. Martin's Press, 1972], pp. 160ff.)

83. *LPP*, pp. 361, 362, 369, 370.

84. *LPP*, p. 232.

85. Drama fragment, above, pp. 29ff. Another example of Bonhoeffer's sensitivity to the wordless response to suffering comes from his prison conversations with Professor Gaetano Latmiral, a fellow inmate in Tegel. Bonhoeffer told Latmiral that during the Nazi regime's forced deportation of Jews from Berlin some elderly Jewish-Christian women asked him if God would reject them if they took their own lives before the Nazis came to remove them from their homes. Pastor Bonhoeffer responded with silence. (Interview with Professor Gaetano Latmiral in Geneva, Switzerland, February 5, 1976.) Later, during the first months in prison, Bonhoeffer himself experienced the temptation to take his own life. See *DB*, p. 736.

86. *LPP*, p. 371.

87. *LPP*, p. 194.

88. Drama fragment, above, p. 14.

89. *DB*, p. 830.

90. For several examples of Bonhoeffer's love of theatre and of children's responses, see Zerner, "Bonhoeffer's American Experiences," pp. 265–266.

91. *DB*, p. 24.

92. *DB*, pp. 23–25. *GS*, 2, pp. 362, 557–558; *WF*, pp. 250, 254ff.

93. Anwar el-Sadat, *In Search of Identity: An Autobiography* (New York: Harper, 1977, 1978), pp. 73, 75.

94. Ibid., pp. 76, 79.

95. *LPP*, p. 129.

96. Malcolm X, *The Autobiography of Malcolm X*, with the assistance of Alex Haley (New York: Ballantine Books, 1964, 1965), pp. 179–180, 391–392.

97. Robert Coles, M.D., *Privileged Ones: The Well-Off and the Rich in America*. Vol. V of *Children of Crisis* (Boston: Atlantic-Little, Brown, 1977).

98. Bernadette Morand, *Les écrits des prisonniers politiques* (Paris: Presses Universitaires de France, 1976), p. 30.

99. *LPP*, p. 311.

100. *LPP*, pp. 279, 347–348.

101. Morand, *Écrits des prisonniers politiques*, p. 30.

102. Irving Greenberg, discussion following his lecture on "The Holocaust" at the 92nd Street "Y" in New York City, February 3, 1977.

103. Elie Wiesel, "Art and Culture after the Holocaust," in *Auschwitz: Beginning of a New Era?, Reflections on the Holocaust*, edited by Eva Fleischner (New York: KTAV Publishing House, The Cathedral of St. John the Divine, and Anti-Defamation League of B'nai B'rith, 1977), p. 411.

104. Nelly Sachs, "Eli: A Mystery Play of the Sufferings of Israel," translated from the German by Christopher Holme, in *O The Chimneys: Selected Poems, including the verse play, Eli* (New York: Farrar, Straus and Giroux, 1967), pp. 313–387.

105. Wiesel, "Art and Culture," p. 411.

106. *LPP*, p. 300.

107. Elie Wiesel, *The Oath* (New York: Avon Books, 1973, 1974).

108. Wiesel, "Art and Culture," p. 410.

109. Krystal, *Massive Psychic Trauma*, p. 281. For a discussion of ego regression and artistic creativity, see Kris, *Psychoanalytic Explorations*, especially pp. 312–318. Supra, notes 18, 53.

110. *LPP*, p. 300.

111. Kris, *Psychoanalytic Explorations*, pp. 83–84.

112. *LPP*, p. 369.

113. *LPP*, p. 346.

Index

SUBJECTS

Index